Breaking the HEC-RAS Code

A User's Guide to Automating HEC-RAS

Breaking the HEC-RAS Code

A User's Guide to Automating HEC-RAS

First Edition

Christopher Goodell, P.E., D.WRE

h2ls
Portland OR

Breaking the HEC-RAS Code: A User's Guide to Automating HEC-RAS
ISBN: 978-0-9908918-0-2
First Edition - Paperback

Published in the United States of America by:

h2ls
Portland, Oregon
www.h2ls.com

To order a copy of this book, please visit:
www.therassolution.com

Sample VBA code for all of the HECRAS Procedures, all code presented in this book, along with numerous example applications can be ordered in electronic form as a single Microsoft® Excel® workbook from The RAS Solution, www.therassolution.com

Disclaimer: No information, written or implied in this book or any resource recommended should be considered advice for any individual or company, but constitutes a general education regarding automation of the software program HEC-RAS. Neither h2ls, nor the author, Christopher Goodell, nor any affiliated entity accepts liability for anyone or anything that uses information presented in this book.

Trademark notice: This book uses various trademarked names within its text. In the interest of trademark holders, this book cites their ownership of the trademarks, with no intention of infringement.

Software information: This book discusses strategies and techniques for automating the software program HEC-RAS. HEC-RAS is developed and distributed free-of-charge by the United States Army Corps of Engineers, Hydrologic Engineering Center in Davis, California. HEC-RAS and its supporting manuals may be downloaded from the Hydrologic Engineering Center's website, www.hec.usace.army.mil.

Cover Art: The photograph on the cover was taken by the author during a field visit in New Jersey, looking for high water marks and evidence of a dam breach flood. The canoe wrapped around a tree not only serves as a valuable high water mark for calibration, but also demonstrates the enormity of the flood that occurred.

FOR WENDY, MAIAH, ABBY, AND KATIE

TABLE OF CONTENTS

FOREWORD

For almost 30 years, I have worked on developing software tools with the goal of making the process of performing complex hydrologic and hydraulic engineering studies easier. When I first started working at the Hydrologic Engineering Center (HEC), there were many separate tools available to perform all kinds of calculations, but they were very difficult to use. HEC had a separate piece of software for each of the following applications: steady flow hydraulics, unsteady flow hydraulics, 2-dimensional flow hydrodynamics, sediment transport analyses, riverine water quality modeling, and hydraulic design of flood control channels. Each tool required its own data input format, had its own unique way of performing hydraulic computations, and its own output file format (which consisted of a simple text file full of numbers). I knew very early on in my career that I wanted to create a single software system that could perform all types of hydraulic calculations and analyses, was easy to use, and was visually-oriented. I was given that opportunity in 1991, and that was the birth of HEC-RAS. As the author and the leader of the HEC-RAS development team, I have been working to further this goal for my entire career.

Not very long after HEC-RAS was first released, Chris Goodell came to work for me as a member of the HEC-RAS team. I specifically hired Chris to work on the development of the sediment transport analysis capabilities in HEC-RAS. Chris very quickly became a key member of our team. He developed the first sediment transport routines within HEC-RAS, and also worked on stable channel design functions, and many other tools in the HEC-RAS hydraulic design module. Unfortunately for us, in 2003, Chris decided he needed to move back to Portland in order to be closer to family, but our working relationship has remained strong since that time.

While I personally think that HEC-RAS is the best hydraulic engineering analysis tool in the world (yes, I am biased) it still, to this day, cannot do everything that a hydraulic engineer may want it to do. People have all kinds of unique applications in which they would like to use the software to solve their specific problem. Unfortunately, the software does not always have the exact capabilities they need. As there is no way HEC could imagine every way in which a user would like to use HEC-RAS, we decided to make an open API (Application Programming Interface) that would allow users to write their own applications, wherein they could use HEC-RAS to solve unique hydraulic engineering problems. This API is called the HEC-RAS Controller (HECRASController).

This book is a tremendous resource that describes the details of the HECRASController and how to use it. The reader is given the big picture covering why to use the HECRASController, what is available in the HECRASController, how it works, and even real world examples (complete with code) that solve many challenging hydraulic engineering applications. The book explains all of the available functions which are exposed within the HECRASController, and then walks through the creation of a simple program that opens HEC-RAS, modifies data input, runs the computations, and retrieves specific output from the HEC-RAS binary output file. The book goes into great detail about how to use the HECRASController to read and write to HEC-RAS input files. Reading and writing to input files is used to automate modifying the input parameters. The book discusses how to monitor the HEC-RAS computations/progress during a run, as well as application strategies. The last part of the book contains detailed examples for solving complex hydraulic problems, complete with the source code, and a step-by-step discussion of what the code does. By learning how to use the HECRASController, users have an opportunity to take the existing hydraulic computational capability in HEC-RAS, and apply it in ways that currently do not exist. This makes it easy to extend HEC-RAS to solve difficult engineering problems, without having to write an entire hydraulic software application from scratch.

This book is the only complete resource that explains how to use the HECRASController in its entirety; and is comprehensive, easy to read, and well-documented. Chris has been writing code around HEC-RAS to solve unique problems for years. He has also suggested several ideas for expanding and improving the HECRASController. Chris has done an outstanding job with this book. Anyone with experience in HEC-RAS and a basic understanding of programming language will be able to use this book to help build applications that control HEC-RAS.

As the author and leader of the HEC-RAS development team, I highly recommend *Breaking the HEC-RAS Code* to anyone who wants to take HEC-RAS and expand its capabilities in order to solve challenging hydraulic engineering problems.

Gary W. Brunner, P.E., D.WRE
Leader of the HEC-RAS Development Team
Hydrologic Engineering Center, USACE
Davis, CA

PREFACE

"Breaking the HEC-RAS Code" has been a true labor of love for me. Some of my most enjoyable times working have been when I've had the opportunity to immerse myself in an HEC-RAS project and have had to rely on experience and creativity to make it work. Like most engineers, writing is well outside my comfort zone. But I found that I really enjoyed writing this book; it seemed that every page I wrote revealed more and more possibilities for automating HEC-RAS using the HECRASController. The HECRASController is a suite of programming procedures included with the installation of HEC-RAS. As HEC-RAS users, we all know how powerful and useful the software is. But we also know (or should know) that it has its limitations-and always will. To me, discovering the HECRASController was like having my own personal HEC-RAS team member- always there, just waiting to implement a new feature or functionality into HEC-RAS for my own personal use. The applications seemed endless. If I could dream it up, it could be done.

Earlier in my career, I worked in California at the Hydrologic Engineering Center on the HEC-RAS Development Team. There, I refined my HEC-RAS "chops", under the guidance and mentorship of Gary Brunner. HEC is also where I first learned about the HECRASController. The potential applications of this relatively unknown feature were not lost on me, and I immediately began using it to automate HEC-RAS processes such as retrieving output, automating input, and batch mode processing. I carried this skill over to my current job at WEST Consultants, where efficiency in hydraulic modeling is not only encouraged, but required to meet the tight budgets ever-so-present in the competitive market of engineering consulting. While at WEST, I have compiled an extensive library of spreadsheet macros that I use frequently to improve the efficiency and quality of my HEC-RAS projects. The techniques I developed were further advanced to proprietary software like WEST-EDI, HBox, and MCBreach-all software that makes extensive use of the HECRASController. Meanwhile, through teaching HEC-RAS classes regularly with the American Society of Civil Engineering Continuing Education Program, and presenting papers at a variety of conferences, I've established myself as an expert in the use of HEC-RAS. Technical support questions from weary and frustrated HEC-RAS users flood my email inbox. To serve that need, I created the HEC-RAS help blog, "The RAS Solution" in 2007. The RAS Solution has become quite popular and my audience is worldwide. The blog currently generates over 22,000 monthly page views and serves as a valuable resource for HEC-RAS modelers. Although not one of the most popular topics on The RAS Solution (mostly because people are just not aware of it), HECRASController questions always generate considerable buzz. Users want to know about it. Those who do know something about it, want to know how to use it more effectively.

Although I have been successful in applying the HECRASController to my projects, I found myself using precious project time learning or re-learning the components of the HECRASController and how they are used in a programming environment. Furthermore, prior to this book, there was no documentation on the HECRASController. In fact, most HEC-RAS users don't even know it exists. Those who have discovered the HECRASController spend frustrating hours trying to figure it out so they can use it for their own projects. That is why I wrote this book.

"Breaking the HEC-RAS Code" is designed to be a manual for HEC-RAS Users. It's not only a "how-to" book, but also serves as a valuable reference for HECRASController users. There are extensive libraries in the appendices that document how to use all of the procedures in the HECRASController with detailed descriptions of their required parameters and what they all mean. An HEC-RAS user writing code to automate HEC-RAS will draw on this reference repeatedly, especially while learning the intricacies of the HECRASController. Furthermore, this book is meant for the typical HEC-RAS user. Professional computer programmers may find the sample code and follow-up discussion elementary. This is by design. I'm attempting to introduce HEC-RAS users to programming code and how it can be used to automate and control HEC-RAS with the HECRASController. Most HEC-RAS users have (at most) a very basic understanding of programming language and limited experience writing code. My aim is not to teach people how to be expert code writers -- there are many books already out there to serve that purpose. The purpose of this book is to give HEC-RAS users the tools to quickly and effectively develop applications that will control and automate HEC-RAS to improve both the quality and efficiency of their projects – and to make HEC-RAS do what it can't do on its own.

Assembling this book has taken years of research and documentation. Much of this book was written during cross-country flights and nights in hotels on business trips. I could not have done it without the help and support of a number of influential people along the way. I want to thank Gary Brunner of the Hydrologic Engineering Center for his mentorship while I worked on the HEC-RAS Team. Gary has been the lead developer of HEC-RAS since the first version was released in 1995. His unparalleled knowledge of HEC-RAS and his valuable insight have helped me tremendously in this effort. I also want to thank Jeff Bradley, President of WEST Consultants, for giving me the opportunity to be an HEC-RAS instructor and for encouraging me to write papers on the subject. Dr. Bradley is a successful businessman, but to my delight, he fosters a work environment that values continuing education and research -- a rarity in the bottom-line oriented consulting world. I would not be in the position to write this book, had it not been for his support. I also want to acknowledge the following people for their help:

- Mark Jensen, lead interface programmer for HEC-RAS and the developer of the HECRASController. He was a tremendous resource for me. When I couldn't figure out a process related to the HECRASController-when I was having trouble "breaking the HEC-RAS code"- Mark made himself available to help.

- The rest of the HEC-RAS Development Team: Steven Piper, Cameron Ackerman, and Stanford Gibson for graciously offering assistance and insight to the variety of HEC-RAS problems I've encountered over the years.

- My wife Wendy and daughters Maiah, Abby, and Katie. Thanks for your encouragement and support, and for putting up with me while I wrote this book.

  My hope is that "Breaking the HEC-RAS Code" will serve as a valuable resource to HEC-RAS modelers all around the globe.

Christopher R. Goodell, P.E., D.WRE

1

WHAT IS HEC-RAS AND WHY DO WE WANT TO CONTROL IT?

The Hydrologic Engineering Center's (HEC) River Analysis System (HEC-RAS) is one of the most popular hydraulic analysis software programs in the world. Engineers, scientists, and students from every corner of the globe have used HEC-RAS to predict water surface elevations in rivers and streams under a variety of different studies including flood defense, flood insurance, bridge and culvert hydraulics, river and stream restoration, river and stream realignment, dam and levee design, dam removal, dam and levee failure, and water supply. It is accepted as a reliable hydraulic model by federal agencies including the Federal Emergency Management Agency (FEMA), the National Weather Service (NWS), the Natural Resource Conservation Service (NRCS), and the U.S. Army Corps of Engineers.

HEC-RAS is developed and maintained by the Hydrologic Engineering Center (HEC) in Davis, California. HEC (officially pronounced H-E-C, although to the displeasure of most HEC staff, it's commonly pronounced "heck") is the Corps of Engineer's center of expertise for surface and groundwater hydrology, river hydraulics, sediment transport, hydrologic statistics and risk analysis, reservoir system analysis, planning analysis, real-time water control management and other closely associated technical subjects (see HEC website, www.hec.usace.army.mil). HEC was established in 1946 to consolidate the Corps' water resources expertise in order to pass it along to new, inexperienced Corps engineers. Immediately following its inception, HEC began offering training courses and developing computer programs which evolved into the, now familiar, HEC software. The early years spawned software programs with very uninteresting names, such as HEC-1, HEC-2, HEC-3, HEC-4, HEC-5, and HEC-6. These were sophisticated programs for their day, using the latest techniques for watershed hydrology, river hydraulics, sediment transport, etc., that would eventually be run on a "new kind of computer" – a desktop P.C. While still usable today, they are run on a DOS platform and, by today's standards, HEC's suite of "numbered" programs are slow, inefficient, and simply outdated. HEC recognized early on the trend towards graphical user interface (GUI) platforms and object-oriented programming and in the early 1990's began development of the Next Generation of hydraulics and hydrology software (NexGen). Thus began HEC-RAS-a replacement to HEC-2. Version 1.0 of HEC-RAS was released in 1995 with a very basic interface appearance and limited capabilities (Figure 1). However, current HEC-RAS users will notice that the overall structure of the GUI has remained very much the same, since its initial release.

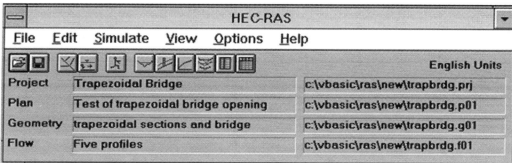

Figure 1. HEC-RAS Version 1.0.

Under the vision and leadership of Gary Brunner, HEC-RAS quickly improved in both quality and functionality. Today it is able to compute in both steady and unsteady flow, and under sub- and supercritical flow regimes. Gary has a unique ability to direct and pursue research and development for HEC-RAS while still maintaining a level of software practicality and usability that helps to make HEC-RAS so popular. HEC-RAS can also compute moveable boundary sediment transport as well as perform water quality analysis. The current version of HEC-RAS (at publication time), Version 5.0, has the option to compute two-dimensional hydraulics to augment the traditional one-dimensional approach. HEC-RAS has superb graphics, and its integration with Geographical Information Systems (GIS) through its companion GIS extension, HEC-GeoRAS, and its built-in RAS Mapper, has made flood mapping and animation of flood wave propagation an easy and very effective way to communicate flood scenarios with the general public. Figure 2 shows the main HEC-RAS window as it looks today, in Version 5.0. The new interface is larger with many more options, but Version 5.0 maintains a very similar look and feel to the original Version 1.0.

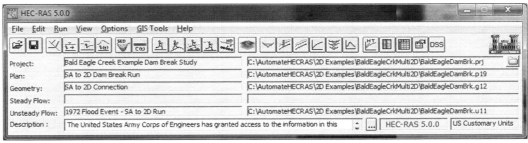

Figure 2. HEC-RAS Version 5.0.

One of the most powerful, yet relatively unknown features available in HEC-RAS is the HECRASController. The HECRASController is part of an HEC-RAS application programming interface (API); a collection of programming classes that contain HEC-RAS-specific functions and subroutines that can be called within programming code during run time.

The current version of the HECRASController has a wealth of procedures that will allow a programmer to manipulate HEC-RAS externally by setting input data, retrieving input or output data, and performing common functions such as opening and closing HEC-RAS, changing plans, running HEC-RAS, and plotting output. While the HECRASController was initially developed to provide third party software an option for incorporating HEC-RAS into their own interfaces, its applicability has expanded for cross platform communication under HEC's Watershed Analysis Tool (WAT) and the Corps Water Management System (CWMS) software. As it stands today, HECRASController applications for the general public, are seemingly endless. Not only can the retrieval and post-processing of output be automated, but with the HECRASController, real-time modeling is possible. Probabilistic exercises, like the Monte Carlo method, a statistical experiment that requires repeated random sampling of input parameters and rerunning of a model up to ten- and even hundreds of thousands of times, become practical ways for quantifying risk and uncertainty and determining probabilities of outcomes using the HECRASController.

This book seeks to explain how the HECRASController works, to provide example applications of the HECRASController, and to catalog the vast array of programming procedures (and how to use them) embedded in the HEC-RAS API. The HEC-RAS API is compiled as a component object model (COM) dynamic link library (DLL). Although the HECRASController is useable by any programming language that can call a

DLL, this book will discuss the HECRASController and present examples of its use from a Visual Basic® programming background. The reason is twofold:

- HEC-RAS is written in Visual Basic® (VB), so the HECRASController has a VB "feel" to it, and

- The programming language behind the popular Macros in Microsoft® Excel® is Visual Basic® for Applications (VBA) – a relative of VB that uses the same Visual Basic® Runtime Library.

Excel® is much more widely used in the engineering community than software writing applications, including Visual Studio®, and it is expected that the majority of the readers of this book will use VBA in Excel® for automating HEC-RAS. This is not to discount the advantages and elegance of creating a stand-alone piece of software that controls HEC-RAS from more sophisticated and robust programming languages. There is certainly a place for that. However, the concepts presented in this book, though presented within the context of programming in VBA, can easily be applied to Visual Basic® or other programming platforms by anyone with a reasonable level of skill in object-oriented software programming.

2

CONTROLLING HEC-RAS

Anyone who has downloaded and installed HEC-RAS (version 3.1 or later) already has access to the HEC-RAS API. The HEC-RAS API is a reference library that contains three publically available classes, each with its own set of procedures (blocks of programming code that perform tasks) designed specifically to facilitate and control the operation and behavior of HEC-RAS, to edit input files, and to read input and output files. The HECRASController is one of these classes. HEC-RAS is compiled as a Component Object Module (COM) server application and its companion HECRASController can be called by any client program that can read a COM DLL. As opposed to a fully contained, stand-alone software application, a client makes requests to another computer program (i.e. HEC-RAS) through programs and libraries in the computer's server (i.e. the HEC-RAS API) taking advantage of already-established procedures. By adding HEC-RAS as a server application reference to your software development project, the HEC-RAS API, and more specifically all of its classes and procedures, becomes available to use in your code. The HEC-RAS API is the server application and the code written to control and automate HEC-RAS makes up the client program.

To access the HEC-RAS API in Excel® (VBA), open the Excel® Visual Basic® Editor by selecting the View tab and clicking on View Macros under the Macro button, or by pressing Alt+F11 on the keyboard. If no macros have been written to the current Excel® Workbook, "View Macro's" will not work. In this case press Alt+F11 or add the "Developer" tab to the menu ribbon at the top of the Excel® window. The Developer tab includes a number of developer tools, including a "Visual Basic" button which will open the Visual Basic® Editor. Once the Visual Basic® Editor is open, select the Tools menu item and then click on References. This brings up a dialog as shown in Figure 3. If there are multiple installations of HEC-RAS (different versions like 3.1.3, 4.0, 4.1, 5.0, etc.), there will be multiple listings of "HEC River Analysis System". Single click on each one and search for the one located in the folder of the version you are interested in, listed in the frame at the bottom of the dialog. Once the correct version is identified, click the check box next to that version and press the OK button on the dialog. The HEC-RAS API will now be accessible in the Visual Basic® Editor in Excel®. Be aware when browsing for the HEC-RAS API. It resides in the HEC-RAS program folder in the Program Files (x86) directory and it has a .exe extension (i.e. ras.exe), not a .dll extension.

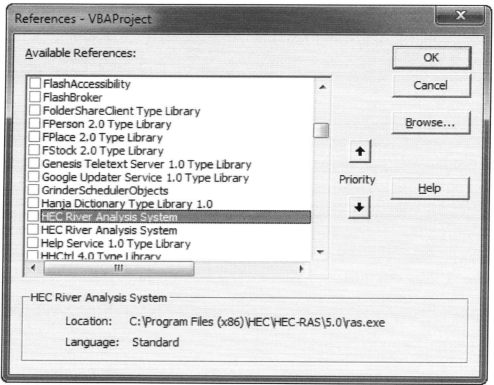

Figure 3. Add Reference Dialog Box in the Visual Basic® Editor of Excel®.

To have access to the HEC-RAS API in Visual Studio®, click on the Properties menu item under Project, on the main Visual Studio® window. Click on the References side tab and then click on the Add button. The Add Reference Dialog will come up and will list all of the references available on the computer. Select the COM tab at the top and browse to HEC River Analysis System as shown in Figure 4.

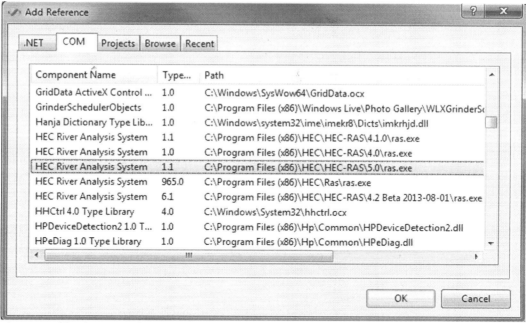

Figure 4. Add Reference Dialog in Visual Studio®.

As with the Visual Basic® Editor in Excel®, the Add Reference dialog in Visual Studio® may show multiple HEC River Analysis System entries. Be sure to select the one from the correct version. The HEC-RAS API will now be accessible in Visual Studio®.

To get an overview of everything available for automating HEC-RAS, view the Object Browser (in the Excel® Visual Basic® Editor, click on View…Object Browser, or simply press the F2 key). The object browser displays all of the programming libraries (i.e. pre-compiled code) that are available to the client program, including the HEC-RAS API. This library will be called RAS500 for Version 5.0 (or something similar for previous versions, i.e.: RAS410, for Version 4.1). Filter out the other libraries in order to have access to and only view the RAS500 library. Three classes are represented: HECRASController, HECRASFlow, and HECRASGeometry. In computer programming, a class is a template definition of an object.

Think of a class as just that-a school classroom. But not a particular classroom, rather a generic classroom that contains typical objects - students, teachers, computers, books, etc. Those objects exist as variables, ready to be populated with specific information by the program. Every classroom has a teacher, and so would a programming class that represents a classroom – let's call it **clsClassroom**. The programming class might contain a string variable called, "**strTeacher**", which would contain the name of the teacher. There might also be a variable called **intTeacherGrade**, which would hold an integer number of the grade level of the teacher's class. Also included could be the teacher's age, the teacher's tenure level, the teacher's license status, and so on. An experienced programmer would recognize these properties are all attributed to the teacher and would therefore set up a sub-class called **clsTeacher** that can be instantiated within the classroom class. That way, all attributes associated with the teacher remain conveniently inside a single "teacher" class. Perhaps there are two teachers in the class. Each teacher could be defined as its own **clsTeacher** class within the **clsClassroom** class. However the **strTeacher** variable might be "Mrs. Jones" for the first teacher and "Mr. Berg" for the second.

In addition to physical objects, a classroom has rules and procedures. So can the **clsClassroom** class. Perhaps there is a procedure for asking a question. It may go something like this:

1. Student raises her hand.

2. If the teacher calls on the student, the student asks the question.

3. If the teacher does not call on the student, the student sits quietly with hand patiently raised.

4. If the student asks her question before the teacher calls on the student, the student is disciplined.

5. The student lowers her hand.

This example represents what could be programmed as a subroutine in **clsClassroom** called **AskAQuestion**.

The classes in the HEC-RAS API are simply collections of procedures that can be called upon by the client program you create. Instead of an **AskAQuestion** subroutine, the HEC-RAS API classes have subroutines that edit input values, retrieve output, and manipulate HEC-RAS. *Table 1* briefly describes the three publically available classes in the HEC-RAS API.

Table 1. Programming Classes available in the HEC-RAS API, Version 5.0.

Class	Description
HECRASController	Procedures and classes for programming level communication with HEC-RAS.
HECRASFlow	One function, "UnsteadyBoundaryIndex".
HECRASGeometry	HEC-RAS Geometry-related procedures.

The HECRASFlow class appears to be a short-lived class construct that isn't really maintained by HEC anymore. The HECRASGeometry class is actually referenced within the HECRASController as a property called Geometry. The HECRASController contains the overwhelming majority of useful procedures for the general HEC-RAS community and therefore the HECRASController will be the primary focus of this book.

The Object Browser is a quick and convenient way to see what procedures, classes, and properties (collectively called "members") are available in the HECRASController. Figure 5 shows the Object Browser and a partial view of the list of members in the HECRASController.

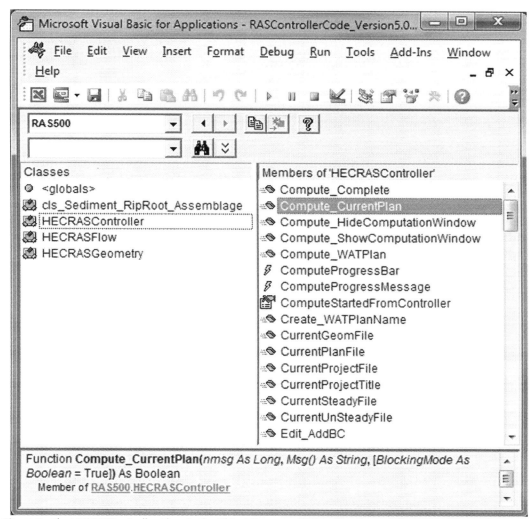

Figure 5. The HECRASController Class in the Object Browser of VBA. Members of the HECRASController.

The HECRASController has over 100 subroutines and functions (collectively referred to in this book as procedures) that can be used to manipulate HEC-RAS from a client program. In developing a program that works with HEC-RAS in some context, there will be one or more procedures that you write yourself (called client code), but there is also access to the API procedures already written and compiled in the HECRASController. Once you reference the HEC-RAS API, the HECRASController code will become, in essence, an extension of your client code. Both Visual Studio® and the Visual Basic® Editor in Excel® offer an autocomplete function that displays a dropdown menu of procedures to choose from when the programmer types a dot (.) after a variable instantiated as a new class. Figure 6 provides an example of this feature. This is very important for the HECRASController since historically there has been no documentation or listing of its available procedures (this book serves as the first comprehensive resource for this information).

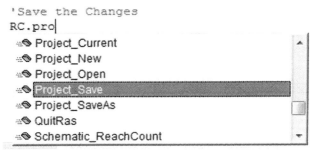

Figure 6. Autocomplete feature.

Variables and Data Types

Writing programming code requires the use of variables. Think of a variable as a container that holds a bit of information. That information is called an argument. Setting, retrieving, and processing information is the essence of computer programming, and so variables play an integral part in any written code. Different information requires different amounts of computer memory for processing in a binary operating system. To maximize computing efficiency, programmers will use appropriate data types for their variables so the minimum amount of computing resources are used. A Boolean type variable is the simplest data type and only requires a single bit of computer memory to define the information it holds. A bit is a unit of information that can be stored in computer memory and can only be one of two values- a 0 or a 1. Booleans are simply either true or false, yes or no, on or off, or in binary speak, 0 or 1. There are only two possible values for a Boolean data type but they still require 8 bits of memory storage in Visual Basic® (a Boolean theoretically only requires 1 bit for binary programming, but most operating systems handle memory in groups of 8 bits (one byte). For a variable whose argument is either true or false, it would be a waste of computing storage to use a Single data type, which requires 32 bits of memory storage.

There are numerous data types available to a programmer, but the HECRASController uses five data types as variables for its procedures. These data types are listed in *Table 2*. Single precision floating-point (Single) data types are most commonly used in the HECRASController for real numbers that are not integers. The term "floating point" refers to the concept of maintaining freedom with regard to the number of digits on either side of the decimal point. The decimal point, in essence, can *float* around the digits of a floating point number. This provides a much larger range of numbers than a fixed point data type. With a range of plus or minus 3.4028235×10^{38} and six to nine significant decimal digits, most numerical values used in HEC-RAS can be stored in a Single data type. The developers of HEC-RAS recognize that occasionally larger numbers may be possible, or (more likely) more decimal digits may be required, and in those cases Double precision floating-point (Double) data types are used. Examples include date/time values in Julien format and geographic coordinate points. In addition, Double data types are becoming more common as variables for non-integer numbers, since computing power and memory availability is much improved now versus the mid-nineties, when HEC-RAS was in its infancy. Using the 64 bits required for a double precision floating point variable is not quite as intrusive to memory storage as it once was.

Project names, river and reach names, river station names, and all other text-based variables in HEC-RAS are stored as strings. With up to 2 billion characters allowed for any one variable, String data types can hold an enormous amount of text. In fact, this entire book could theoretically be stored as one String variable!

Although Integer data types are commonly used in Visual Basic® programming, the developers of HEC-RAS have elected to exclusively use Long data types to store integer numbers. Long data types work exactly like integers, except they use 64 bits of memory, while integers only use 32. This provides the ability to work with much larger numbers.

It's important to understand the limitations of various data types, since these will be used frequently when calling procedures within the HECRASController. While writing code for your own application, you are free to use any data type available within the programming language you are working with; Visual Basic® has many more data types than are found in the HECRASController. However, when calling HECRASController procedures in your code, make certain to use data types consistent with their required variables (called "parameters" in Visual Basic® speak). Do this by either declaring them consistently in the code initially, or converting them prior to passing them in the call.

Table 2. *Data types used in the HECRASController (Reference MSDN® Library, http://msdn.microsoft.com).*

Data Type	Bits of Memory	Range	Proximity to Zero	Significant Decimal Digits	Description
Boolean	8	0 or 1	Na	Na	Used to describe the state of a variable as either 0/1, true/false, on/off, yes/no.
Single	32	$+\text{-}3.403 \times 10^{38}$	$+\text{-}1.401 \times 10^{-45}$	6 to 9	A single precision floating point number.
Double	64	$+\text{-}1.798 \times 10^{308}$	$+\text{-}4.941 \times 10^{-324}$	15 to 17	A double precision floating point number.
String	16*	0 to 65535*	Na	Na	A sequence of characters (i.e. letters, numbers, punctuation, etc.). Each character is represented by an integer number from 0 to 65535. A string can hold up to 2 billion characters.
Long	64	$+\text{-}9.223 \times 10^{18}$	+-1	0	Integers. HEC-RAS uses Long data types instead of Integers (in VB, Long data types use 64 bits versus 32 for integers, so larger numbers can be stored).

*Per character.

Subroutines

A subroutine is a block of code that performs a sequence of tasks. Generally, in the HECRASController, each subroutine performs one task. The HECRASController code that performs this task is not visible, only the name of the subroutine itself. The code is compiled and embedded in the HEC-RAS API. Unfortunately, this makes the HECRASController somewhat of a "black box" in that there is no way of seeing how the task is performed. Some subroutines require information, called "arguments", to be supplied by the client code (this information is passed as parameters), while others require no arguments at all. For example, one of the simplest subroutines in the HECRASController, **Project_Save**, will save whatever HEC-RAS project is currently open. No arguments are required by the HECRASController to run this subroutine. **Project_Open**, on the other hand, requires the project file name, including its path, so that the HECRASController knows which project to open. In this case, a String parameter, called **ProjectFileName** must be passed as an argument to the **Project_Open** subroutine. For a simple program, the user may elect to hard code in the name of the

12

project to open. This is more common if the program is written for a specific HEC-RAS project and is not expected to be used for any other projects. A more versatile program may request the user to provide the project name to an input box or select the project name from a dialog. The selected project name is then passed to the **Project_Open** subroutine as the argument for the **ProjectFileName** parameter. In Visual Basic®, arguments to be passed to a subroutine are defined in parameters listed after the call to that subroutine *without* parentheses. The following simple code demonstrates the **Project_Open** subroutine as it might appear in a VBA program:

```
Dim RC As New HECRASController
Dim strFilename As String

strFilename = "C:\ExampleRASProjects\BeavCrek.prj"
RC.Project_Open strFilename
```

The HECRASController is a class of subroutines and functions. To access that class, you must first create a new instance of, or *instantiate* an object as, the HECRASController. In the first line of code above, **RC** becomes the instantiated object of the type **HECRASController**. All programming procedures that will use the HECRASController must either receive a parameter already instantiated as an HECRASController, or must instantiate it within the procedure itself. Most blocks of code presented in this book will begin with "Dim RC As New HECRASController". The next line, "Dim strFilename As String", defines the variable "strFilename" as a String data type. "strFilename" is the name of a String variable that contains the project path and filename. Though not required, adding the prefix "str" to the string variable is a common variable naming convention used in modern programming, called *Hungarian Notation*. The idea being that prefixes make it easy to quickly identify what data type a given variable is. Single data types have the prefix "sng", Doubles: "dbl", Longs: "lng", Booleans: "bln", etc. The variable "strFilename" is then assigned a string value in the third line of code; in this case the path and filename of the HEC-RAS project to open. Finally, in the fourth line of code, the variable "strFilename" is passed with the argument "C:\ExamplesRASProjects\BeavCrek.prj" as the parameter to the HECRASController subroutine **Project_Open**. Notice in the code the parameter resides after the subroutine call, <u>without</u> parentheses.

It's important to consider the location where **RC** is declared as a new HECRASController, while writing code. By default, any variable declared within a procedure will only "live" in that procedure. As soon as that procedure is completed, the memory allocated to the variable **RC** will be released, and **RC** will no longer exist as an HECRASController in the code. When a variable is instantiated as a new HECRASController, all of the procedures within the HECRASController are now part of that variable. But, until the **Project_Open** subroutine is called, HEC-RAS will not be open as a *process* in Windows®. Then, once the **ShowRAS** subroutine is called, HEC-RAS will be opened as an active *application* in the Windows® operating system. Until the **ShowRAS** subroutine is called, you won't see HEC-RAS open on the desktop and it won't be available to interact with, but it is nevertheless opened in the background as a process. This can be verified by opening the Windows® Task Manager (Ctrl-Alt-Delete) and viewing the active processes. During program run-time, if you pause the code with a breakpoint after you call the **Project_Open** subroutine, you will see ras.exe as an active process in the Task Manager (Figure 7). When the **ShowRAS** subroutine is called, it will show up as an application in the Task Manager (Figure 8), and will be open on the Windows® desktop. At any time in the code, if the **QuitRas** subroutine is called, HEC-RAS will close as a Windows® application, but remain open in the background as a process. Not until the **End Sub** (or **End Function**) command is called will HEC-RAS cease to run as a process. It's a wise idea to always end a subroutine with **QuitRas**, to avoid stacking multiple ras.exe processes in the background, gobbling up valuable computer resources. However, once that subroutine is completed (at the **End Sub** command), HEC-RAS will close and exit (without warning).

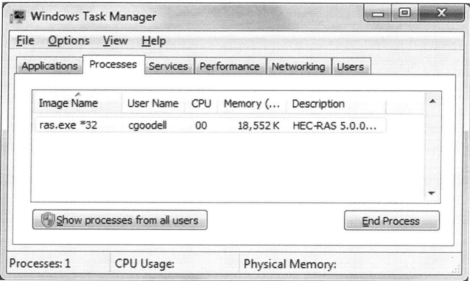

Figure 7. HEC-RAS listed as an active process in the Windows® Task Manager.

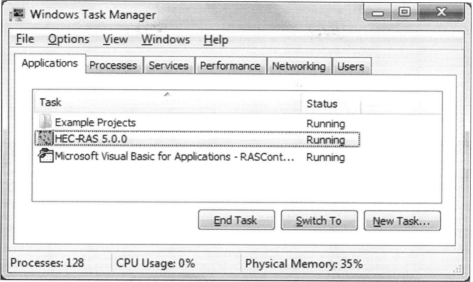

Figure 8. HEC-RAS listed as an active application in the Windows® Task Manager.

Functions

Functions are procedures that return information that can be used by the client code. More specifically, a function takes some input data, performs calculations using that input data, and then returns a result. Like subroutines in the HECRASController, the programmer cannot see the code behind the function, only the name of the function itself. Also similar to subroutines, some functions will require arguments to be passed from the referencing code, while others will not. The primary difference between a subroutine and a function is that a function will return a value directly to the referencing code. Some of the most useful functions in the HECRASController are the "Information" functions, in that they return information about the current HEC-RAS project. This could be anything from the name of the project, to the currently active plan, to the number of steady flow water surface profiles that are available to view. **CurrentProjectTitle** is a function in the HECRASController that returns the name of the title for the active HEC-RAS project. No arguments are required to be passed to **CurrentProjectTitle**; it simply returns the name of the HEC-RAS project title. Because functions return information, they are themselves variables and have to be assigned a variable type. **CurrentProjectTitle** is a string type, since it returns a sequence of characters that make up the title name.

Functions as Subroutines

Some functions in the HECRASController work more like subroutines; they are set up as Boolean type functions, with the return value being true or false, indicating whether the function execution was successful or not. This is particularly useful for debugging or incorporating error checking into the code. If something goes wrong inside a Boolean type function, rather than crashing, it will return a "false" value. **Plan_SetCurrent** is an example of a Boolean type function in the HECRASController. **Plan_SetCurrent** changes the current plan in the active HEC-RAS project to the plan defined as the argument to the function. This acts more like a subroutine, in that there really is no data to return to the client code-it only changes the current plan in the active HEC-RAS project. However, **Plan_SetCurrent** is defined as a Boolean type and it returns either a true or false value, depending on whether or not it was successful in changing the plan to the specified new plan. An action that would trigger a false value to be returned might be passing a string type variable that is not a name of a plan in the active HEC-RAS project. The code behind the **Plan_SetCurrent** function presumably searches the active HEC-RAS project's input file. If it doesn't find that specified plan name, then it is not able to change to that plan, and a false value is returned. The following simple code demonstrates the **Plan_SetCurrent** function as it might appear in a VBA program:

```
Dim RC As New HECRASController
Dim strNewPlanName As String
Dim blnDidItCompute As Boolean

strNewPlanName = "Plan 1 Existing Conditions"
blnDidItCompute = RC.Plan_SetCurrent(strNewPlanName)
```

First the new HECRASController is instantiated as object **RC**, then "**strNewPlanName**" is defined as a string type. "**blnDidItCompute**" is defined as a Boolean that will be set equal to the value returned by the **Plan_SetCurrent** function. Prior to calling the **Plan_SetCurrent** function, "**strNewPlanName**" is populated with the title of the plan to set to current. Notice that when the function is called on the last line of the code, the parameter, **strNewPlanName**, is encapsulated in parentheses.

In VBA, functions can be called in the same way as a subroutine, if you are not concerned with the function's returned value. In this case, to set the current plan, write:

```
RC.Plan_SetCurrent strNewPlanName
```

Notice that when written this way, the parameter is not encapsulated in parentheses.

Subroutines as Functions

Just like some functions that work like subroutines, there are some subroutines in the HECRASController that work like functions, in that they can return information to the client code. Subroutines cannot be set as data types as functions can, but their parameters can be set as reference parameters. When a parameter is set as a reference, its value defined in the subroutine is maintained outside the scope of that subroutine. An advantage here is that more than one variable can be set in the subroutine and returned to the client code. Arrays are common parameter types that are sent to HECRASController subroutines by reference. An array is a variable that can contain multiple values of the same data type and is defined in code with open and closed parentheses. A list of all of the River Stations in a geometry file is an example of data that can be stored in a reference array. **Geometry_GetRivers** is an example of a subroutine that acts like a function and is demonstrated in a simple procedure below.

```
Sub Geometry_GetRivers()

    Dim RC As New HECRASController
    Dim lngRiv As Long
    Dim strRiv() As String

    'Open a RAS project
    OpenRASProjectByRef RC

    'Get an array of rivers.
    RC.Geometry_GetRivers lngRiv, strRiv()

    'Now generate a string that lists all of the rivers _
        separated by a comma.
    Dim i As Integer
    Dim strListOfRivers As String

    For i = 1 To lngRiv
        strListOfRivers = strListOfRivers & strRiv(i) & ", "
    Next i

    MsgBox strListOfRivers

End Sub
```

RC is set to a new instance of the HECRASController class. The first action in this code is to open an existing HEC-RAS project by calling the **OpenRASProjectByRef** subroutine. I wrote this separate subroutine to select an existing HEC-RAS project file already input to a specific cell in an Excel® spreadsheet. In this example, the HEC-RAS project name is input to cell "C4" in the "RASProjects" sheet.

```
Sub OpenRASProjectByRef(ByRef RC As HECRASController)

    'Opens a RAS project by calling from another subroutine
    Dim strFilename As String

    Sheets("RASProjects").Select
    strFilename = Range("C4").Value
    RC.Project_Open Filename

End Sub
```

Prior to executing the code, the user will fill in cell "C4" with the name of the project he or she wishes to work with. Since **RC** is passed as an HECRASController by reference, then after **OpenRASProjectByRef** is complete and the code returns to the **Geometry_GetRivers** subroutine, the RC remains active, and the HEC-RAS project remains open and available for retrieving the River names. **Geometry_GetRivers** has two reference parameters, **nRivers** and **Rivers()**. In the example procedure, **lngRiv** and **strRiv()** are declared as Long and String data types and are passed as arguments for the reference parameters. **nRivers** is the number of rivers in the active geometry file and this parameter is defined as a Long data type (**lngRiv**) in the client code before **Geometry_GetRivers** is called. Likewise, **Rivers()** is a parameter that is defined as a String array (**strRiv()**) prior to calling the subroutine. **Rivers()**, for example, can contain one or more strings, each representing the name of a river in the active geometry file. Before an array is populated, the code must specify the number of elements that will be assigned to the array. Once this is done, an index number (an integer) can be placed within the array variable's parentheses to identify a given value in an array. For example, a geometry file may contain five rivers. The **strRiv()** array will be redimensioned with five String values, each representing the name of one of the rivers, and each receiving its own index number. **strRiv(1)** then represents the first river in the geometry file (contemporary programming prefers the base index of arrays to be 0, versus 1, which can get a bit confusing when writing code, but to date the HECRASController still uses a base index of 1, with a few exceptions). When calling **Geometry_GetRivers**, the user only needs to define the data type. Once the array is passed to the subroutine, the HECRASController will redimension and populate it prior to sending it back to the referencing code. Because it is a reference parameter, **Rivers()** will maintain its values even after it leaves the scope of **Geometry_GetRivers** and is sent back to the client code. The second half of the example code takes the river names in the **strRiv()** array and displays them in a message box.

HECRASController Parameters

One of the challenges in working with the HECRASController, is knowing what types of parameters are referenced in its subroutines and functions. This book serves as a guide for this information; Appendix A lists all of the reference parameters and their respective arguments for each subroutine and function in the HECRASController. There is also a convenient feature available in Visual Studio® and Visual Basic® for Applications that will assist in determining the types of parameters required for all of the subroutines and functions. In VBA, this feature is called "Auto Quick Info" and can be turned on in the Tools...Options window under the "Editor" tab (Figure 9).

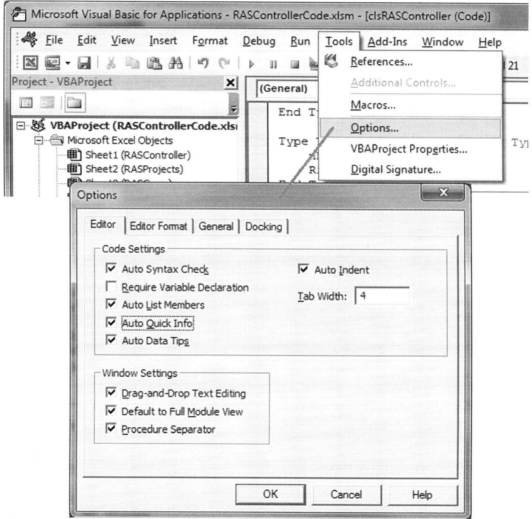

Figure 9. Auto Quick Info Feature.

When Auto Quick Info is enabled, useful information will be revealed as code is written, including the parameters and their respective variable types that are required for a given procedure. In a line of code, if an external procedure is typed, the Auto

Quick Info feature will provide a tool tip information box that lists the parameters and their data types that the HECRASController is expecting, as shown in the following example:

```
RC.Geometry_GetRivers  lngRiv, strRiv()
    Geometry_GetRivers(nRiver As Long, river() As String)
```

Notice that after **RC.Geometry_GetRivers** is typed, the tool tip information box appears. The information in this box reveals two important pieces of information to the programmer:

1. It indicates that **Geometry_GetRivers** is a recognized procedure in the HECRASController, instantiated as **RC** in this case.

2. It tells the programmer what parameters **Geometry_GetRivers** requires (in this case **nRiver** and **river()** are the only parameters required), and what data types the arguments should be (in this case **nRiver** requires a Long data type and **river()** requires a String array. We know that **river()** is an array because of the open and closed parentheses.).

HECRASController Classes and Categories

In addition to the procedures in the HECRASController, there are also groups of procedures, called classes (or sub-classes). Within the current version of HECRASController class, there is one sub-class called **Geometry**. The **Geometry** sub-class is actually a function declared as an HECRASGeometry class. Within the HECRASGeometry class, there are 13 functions and three subroutines, all dealing with geometry in the HEC-RAS project. Most provide information about the components within the active geometry file, such as names and numbers of rivers and reaches, or numbers and types of nodes.

Aside from the pre-defined classes, there are definite groups of similar types of procedures. This book has grouped procedure types into six different categories: Information, Action, Edit Input, Output, Plot, and Tabulate.

Information procedures provide information about the contents and construction of an HEC-RAS model. This could include information about how many rivers are in the active geometry file or what version of HEC-RAS the model was constructed in.

Action procedures prompt HEC-RAS to perform an action. **Project_Open** is an example of an action procedure that simply opens up an HEC-RAS project.

Edit procedures allow the programmer to edit the input files-typically the plan, flow, and geometry files. Some of these procedures will go directly to the input file and change data based on arguments passed by the referencing code (e.g. **Geometry_SetMann**, which sets Manning's n values for a given cross section). Others open up an HEC-RAS editor window so the user can edit input data directly in the HEC-RAS form (e.g. **Edit_XS**, which opens the HEC-RAS cross section editor window).

Output procedures retrieve data from the HEC-RAS output file or the DSS file for the active plan. For these procedures to work, there must be an output file or DSS file to read from (some procedures retrieve data from the output file, some retrieve data from the DSS file). Therefore the active plan has to have been computed prior to calling these procedures. If one of these procedures is called, and no output file or DSS file exists, the HECRASController will return a message indicating it could not retrieve data from the output file (Figure 10). For this reason, it's a good idea to call the subroutine **Compute_CurrentPlan** into any code prior to calling an Output procedure. When calling procedures that retrieve data from the DSS file, only the unsteady flow computations are required. Since the DSS file is created prior to running the post-processing, no post processing is required. **OutputDSS_GetStageFlow** is an example of a function that reads from the DSS file.

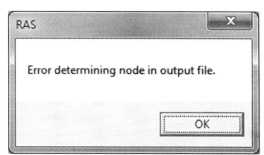

Figure 10. Error message returned when an Output procedure is called, but there is no output file.

Plot procedures will open up a specified HEC-RAS plot window and plot the requested data. Examples include **PlotXS** and **PlotXYZ**.

Tabulate procedures will open up a specified HEC-RAS table and present the requested data in table form. The two tabulate procedures in the current version of the HECRASController are **TableXS** and **TablePF**, which plot the cross section table (also called the Detailed Output Table) table and the profile table (also called the Summary Output Table).

The Edit Subroutines

The HECRASController has a series of subroutines that start with "Edit." As the name implies, they are designed for editing input data in the active HEC-RAS project. Four specific subroutines are designed to add a new component to the geometry:

1. **Edit_AddBC** – Adds a new crossing (bridge, culvert, or multiple opening).

2. **Edit_AddIW** – Adds a new inline structure (IW stands for "Inline Weir", the old HEC-RAS moniker for inline structures).

3. **Edit_AddLW** – Adds a lateral structure (LW stands for "Lateral Weir", the old HEC-RAS moniker for inline structures).

4. **Edit_AddXS** – Adds a new cross section.

To call one of these "Edit Add" subroutines, an existing river and reach must be passed as arguments. Since these subroutines add a new node to the geometry a new river station is also required as an argument. Finally, an empty reference string is required as an argument for any errors the HECRASController wants to send back to the client code.

In HEC-RAS, a node is any feature that occupies a discrete location on a river reach, spatially ordered on that reach by a numerical string value – the *River Station*. There are six node types, listed in *Table 3* along with their respective HECRASController **Edit_Add** subroutines. The node type indices are particularly important to know when reading and writing to/from the HEC-RAS geometry input text file, since the node type is defined in the input file by the index number assigned to it.

Table 3. HEC-RAS Node Types and their Edit_Add subroutines.

Node Type Index	Node Type	Edit_Add Subroutine
1	Cross Section	**Edit_AddXS**
2	Culvert	**Edit_AddBC**
3	Bridge	**Edit_AddBC**
4	Multiple Opening	**Edit_AddBC**
5	Inline Structure	**Edit_AddIW**
6	Lateral Structure	**Edit_AddLW**

If you scan through any HEC-RAS geometry file, using a text editor, the first line in a block of data that represents a node is: "Type RM Length L Ch R =". The number that directly follows the "equals" sign is the node type index and that tells HEC-RAS what type of node it is reading into memory. A node type index of "3", for example, is a bridge. Reading and writing to/from HEC-RAS input files is covered in more detail in Chapter 4.

The Edit subroutines are designed to open an editor window in HEC-RAS so that a user can manually enter data into that editor. Each of the four **Edit_Add** subroutines listed above have a companion **Edit** subroutine, so that once the geometric component is added, input can be entered for it. For example, a program may want to add a culvert (node type 2) to an existing HEC-RAS project, so it calls the **Edit_AddBC** subroutine. After the culvert is added, the **Edit_BC** subroutine is called, which will open the Bridge and Culvert Editor from the HEC-RAS Geometry window, allowing the user to enter data for the culvert directly into the HEC-RAS GUI. Besides the four **Edit_Add** subroutines listed in *Table 3*, there are 12 **Edit** subroutines:

1. **Edit_BC** – Opens the Bridge and Culvert Editor for user edits.

2. **Edit_GeometricData** – Opens the Geometry Schematic for user edits.

3. **Edit_IW** – Opens the Inline Structure Editor for user edits.

4. **Edit_LW** – Opens the Lateral Structure Editor for user edits.

5. **Edit_MultipleRun** – Opens the Run Multiple Plans Dialog for user edits.

6. **Edit_PlanData** – Opens the Steady or Unsteady Flow Analysis Window (whichever plan is active).

7. **Edit_QuasiUnsteadyFlowData** – Opens the Quasi Unsteady Flow Editor for user edits.

8. **Edit_SedimentData** – Opens the Sediment Data Editor for user edits.

9. **Edit_SteadyFlowData** – Opens the Steady Flow Editor for user edits.

10. **Edit_UnsteadyFlowData** – Opens the Unsteady Flow Editor for user edits.

11. **Edit_WaterQualityData** – Opens the Water Quality Data Editor for user edits.

12. **Edit_XS** – Opens the Cross Section Editor for user edits.

There are some quirks to be aware of when using the **Edit_Add** subroutines. First, the river station that is passed as the argument for the **RS** parameter must not already exist in the specified river/reach for the active geometry file. If it does, HEC-RAS will throw an error message that must be clicked to continue the code (Figure 11). Once clicked, the code will resume, but HEC-RAS will not overwrite the existing river station.

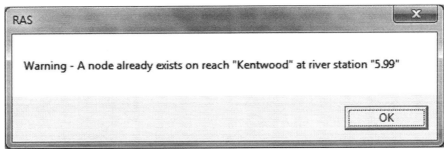

Figure 11. Warning message thrown if an existing river station is used for the newly added feature.

Also, the **Edit_Add** subroutines require their companion **Edit** subroutines be called after the feature is added, but within the same scope that the HECRASController is instantiated. When the edit window opens, there must be some edit action by the user (enter some input data for the feature) taken for HEC-RAS to save that structure. If the companion **Edit** subroutine is not called or no editing action is performed, the new feature will not be saved in the geometry file.

Run-time interruption is an important consideration when using the **Edit** subroutines. Perhaps one of the **Edit** subroutines is called because the user wants to manually enter some input data. If there's no run-time interruption, the program will continue to step through code, line by line, while the editing window is open, and as soon as the end of the procedure is reached, HEC-RAS will close. In most cases this happens so fast, that the user doesn't even notice that the editor window opened up. There's no chance there will be time to enter any data. Therefore, run-time interruption must be written into the code to manually pause run-time to give the user time to enter data. Four of the Edit subroutines have built-in run-time interruption and the run-time will automatically pause when these windows are open: **Edit_BC**, **Edit_GeometricData**, **Edit_IW**, **Edit_LW**, and **Edit_XS**. Once these windows are closed by the user, run-time will resume. For the other **Edit** subroutines that don't automatically pause, run-time interruption is required. This can be accomplished by calling a message box that requires the user to click "OK" to resume run-time. The following subroutine provides an example where the Unsteady Flow Analysis window is opened for editing.

```
Sub EditPlanData()

    'Open a Project
    Dim RC As New HECRASController
    OpenRASProjectByRef RC

    'Open the Unsteady Flow Analysis Window
```

```
RC.Edit_PlanData

'Call a message box to interrupt run-time.
MsgBox "Click OK when done editing the Unsteady Flow " & _
    "Analysis Window."

'Save the changes
RC.Project_Save

End Sub
```

All of the **Edit** procedures in the HEC-RAS API along with their required parameters and a description are listed in Appendix A.

The Geometry Procedures

The HEC-RAS API contains a series of geometry-related procedures that reside both in the HECRASController class and the HECRASGeometry class. In the HECRASController class, the geometry procedures all start with "**Geometry_**". Most of these procedures are informational, in that they simply return some information about geometry data in the current plan. For example, the **Geometry_GetNode** function returns the node index for a passed River Station - nothing is added or edited in the geometry file. Do not confuse the node index with the node type index. The former is an integer number (1 to n, n being the number of nodes in a river/reach) that orders the nodes in a river/reach, while the latter is an integer number (1 to 6) that defines the type of the node, as defined in *Table 3*.

The HECRASGeometry class also contains a series of procedures. An example is the **RiverIndex** function, which returns the river index number, given the passed String argument, "RiverName". With the exception of the Save subroutine which saves the data in the geometry file, all of the procedures in the HECRASGeometry class are informational. To access these procedures in your code, either instantiate a variable as a new HECRASGeometry class:

```
Dim clsGeo As New HECRASGeometry
```

or call directly from the HECRASController class by typing "Geometry" followed by a period, after the instantiated HECRASController object. The Geometry variable is already instantiated as an HECRASGeometry sub-class in the HECRASController class:

```
lngRiverIndex = RC.Geometry.RiverIndex(strRiverName)
```

Once the period is typed after "Geometry", the autocomplete feature in VBA will provide a drop-down box that lists all procedures in the Geometry class, as shown in Figure 12.

```
Dim lngRiverIndex As Long
lngRiverIndex = RC.Geometry.
```

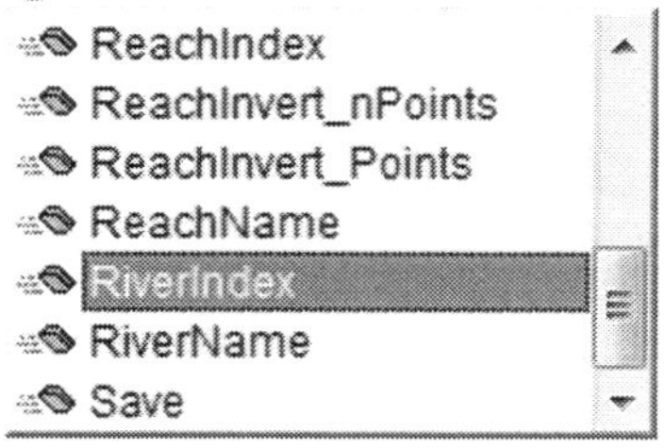
ReachIndex
ReachInvert_nPoints
ReachInvert_Points
ReachName
RiverIndex
RiverName
Save

Figure 12. Auto-complete feature for the Geometry Class.

All of the Geometry procedures in the HEC-RAS API along with their required parameters and a description are listed in Appendix A.

The Output Procedures

The HECRASController class contains a set of procedures that communicate directly with HEC-RAS output files. Since HEC-RAS saves output in binary files, these procedures are the only option for automating the direct retrieval of output data. Unlike ASCII-encoded text files where common language is used to store data in an organized and readable fashion (HEC-RAS input files, for example), binary files cannot be read by humans. If you've ever opened up a binary file in a text editor you've seen what appears to be a jumbled, incoherent mess of symbols and characters, perhaps similar to the example shown below:

```
ÎÏVCš™XCÎÏVCžÉ□žÉ□žÉ□ÀM$ÀžÉ□ÀM$À
XXŠ@v;ç?²rî=s-':}ÆÀ>*Ï◂;žÉ ←êÄ>
¿™Ø>aØZ>k┬?C¢",BC          ABR^ÇB€
```

Figure 13. Example of binary code from a HEC-RAS output file.

It's not really a jumbled, incoherent mess, it just looks that way to humans. This is the ASCII representation of a binary file. Fortunately the output procedures can decipher the output binary files and provide meaningful output that can be used in a program.

Perhaps you want to develop an application that optimizes the operation of tide gates for both fish passage and flood risk reduction. This application would need to execute HEC-RAS for a small segment (maybe 15 minutes or so) of the tide cycle, retrieve velocity and stage at specific locations, run an algorithm that optimizes gate openings for fish-friendly velocities and a maximum allowable stage, and then adjust the gate settings before re-executing HEC-RAS for the next segment of the tide cycle. This would be repeated for one or more full tide cycles to evaluate the performance of the tide gate design. The important step of retrieving output during run-time can only be achieved by using the Output procedures in the HECRASController class.

As one might expect, to use the Output procedures, there must be an output file to read, therefore HEC-RAS has to have been executed at least once before calling an output procedure. Therefore, the **Compute_CurrentPlan** subroutine is generally called prior to calling output procedures.

The Output procedures read from two different HEC-RAS files: the output file itself, designated with the extension .O##, where the ## number represents the HEC-RAS plan the output file is associated with, and the DSS file, designated with the extension .dss.

Only two procedures read from the DSS file and they are the **OutputDSS_GetStageFlow** and **OutputDSS_GetStageFlowSA** functions. The first populates an array of stage values and an array of flow values for a specified cross section, while the second does the same for a storage area.

The rest of the Output procedures read from the output file. Many of these return information about the model geometry itself – information like the names of rivers, reaches, and nodes. This information can also be accessed from the Geometry procedures. Since the Geometry procedures do not require an output file be read, it's generally easier to get geometric information that way.

The **Output_NodeOutput** and **Output_ReachOutput** will be the workhorses for any application that interacts with HEC-RAS output. These two subroutines can retrieve any of the 268 HEC-RAS output variables from the output file for any cross section and any profile. The available output variables in HEC-RAS are numerous- more than even the most experienced HEC-RAS users will ever use. They include some of the more useful hydraulic parameters such as conveyance, velocity, shear stress, and hydraulic radius. Also included are some obscure variables such as alpha energy weighting coefficient, ice thickness, and water surface elevation accounting for air entrainment. There are some differences between the two output retrieval procedures: **Output_NodeOutput** retrieves output for one node only, whereas the **Output_ReachOutput** retrieves output for all nodes in a given reach. Also, **Output_ReachOutput** orders the array of cross sections with the downstream-most cross section first (i.e. the cross section at the downstream end of the reach gets index "1".

One of the arguments passed to the **Output_NodeOutput** and **Output_ReachOutput** functions is a Long number representing the HEC-RAS variable ID number that is being requested.   All 268 HEC-RAS variables, their ID numbers and descriptions are presented in Appendix E.

3

WRITING A SIMPLE PROGRAM

The applications using the HECRASController are near endless: simple programs that run HEC-RAS plans in batch mode to complex Monte Carlo simulations for probabilistic analyses. The user is only limited by programming skill, creativity, knowledge of HEC-RAS, and understanding of the HECRASController. This book aims to provide the reader with enough understanding of the HECRASController to take on even the most complex HEC-RAS automation exercises.

The previous chapter introduced the library of classes and procedures found in the HEC-RAS API. Knowledge of the HEC-RAS API components will allow you to start writing programs that can automate, manipulate, communicate with, and otherwise control HEC-RAS. This chapter will illustrate how to use the HEC-RAS API components to write a simple client program that automates the execution of HEC-RAS, retrieves output, and organizes that output in an Excel® spreadsheet. The simple program, called "GetWSELandVelocity" will open the HEC-RAS example project "Single Bridge – Example 2, BEAVCREK.prj" (that comes with every installation of HEC-RAS), execute the model, and create a spreadsheet listing all of the cross sections and their computed water surface elevations and average velocities. This program is written in an Excel® module using VBA programming language.

The VBA Environment

To begin, open Excel® and enter the VBA Environment by pressing Alt-F11 or by clicking on the Visual Basic® button under the DEVELOPER tab. If the DEVELOPER tab is not already present in your list of menu items, you can add it by accessing the Excel® Options under the File menu item and selecting Customize Ribbon. Check the box next to the Developer tab so that it shows up on in your list of menu items. The DEVELOPER tab provides quick access to the VBA Code Editor as well as a host of other programming options and tools. The VBA editor will look like Figure 14 when it's opened for the first time.

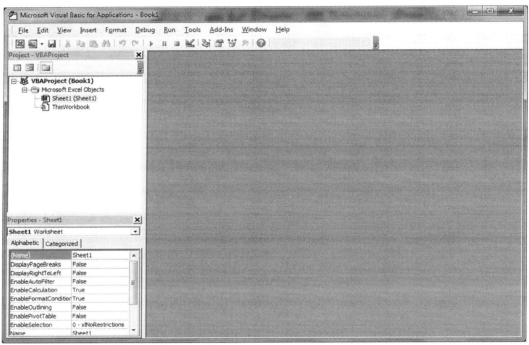

Figure 14. Visual Basic® for Applications Editor.

If a module doesn't already exist, add one by clicking Insert…Module from the Visual Basic® Editor. A new module will be added and the space to the right of the window will be ready for programming code. The name of the module can be changed in the properties window (Figure 15). Before accessing the HEC-RAS API, it must be added as a reference. In the Visual Basic® for Applications window, select Tools…References from the menu items. A window that lists all of the available reference libraries will come up as shown in Figure 16. Look for the HEC River Analysis System reference and check the box next to it.

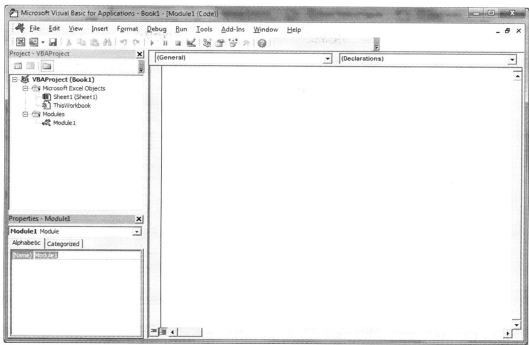

Figure 15. Visual Basic® for Applications Editor with a New Module.

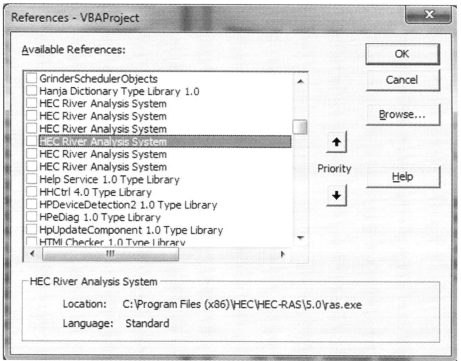

Figure 16. Add Reference Window.

If there is no reference for HEC River Analysis System, then HEC-RAS needs to be installed on the computer. If there are multiple versions of HEC-RAS installed on the computer, there will be multiple entries for HEC River Analysis System. Make sure to check the one for the version of HEC-RAS being used.

Writing the Code

Once the HEC River Analysis System reference is added, you will have access to the HEC-RAS API and all of its classes and procedures. To begin writing code, click in the code window and type:

```
Sub GetWSELandVelocity()
```

Press return and VBA will automatically write the companion **End Sub** command. It's good practice to write some commentary throughout your code, including the author and date of the code and a description of what the subroutine will accomplish. Commentary is defined by placing an apostrophe (') before some text. VBA will automatically color commentary with green font. Good programmers will include comments often throughout their code, liberally describing each block of code, and what its purpose is. My general rule of thumb is to provide enough comments so that someone who may inherit my code in the future will be able to understand what the procedure does, without explanation from me.

The next step is to instantiate a new variable as an HECRASController class by typing:

```
Dim RC As New RAS500.HECRASController
```

Typing the RAS500 before HECRASController is optional, if the RAS500 library is already referenced. Instantiating a new HECRASController makes all of the procedures within the HECRASController class available to use in the new program. After this command, typing "**RC.**" will reveal the procedures in the autocomplete window that VBA provides as a convenience. Your code should now look like the following example. Notice at the end of the comment line that starts with "This subroutine opens..." there is an underscore (_). The underscore is a technique used in VB programming that allows the code writer to continue a single command on successive lines. This works not only for commentary, but for all types of code. Typically, a new line means a new command, but the underscore allows for a single command to be wrapped on multiple lines. This technique is prevalent throughout the examples in this book, so that the sample code will fit within the book margins and still be legible. It's not required for programming in VB or VBA, but it is good practice and can make the code easier to read.

```
Sub GetWSELandVelocity()
```

```
'Instantiate a new RAS500.HECRASController Class
Dim RC As New RAS500.HECRASController
```

Opening HEC-RAS

Opening the HEC-RAS project requires a call to the **Project_Open** subroutine. The **Project_Open** subroutine requests an argument for the HEC-RAS project you wish to open, which is a string variable including both the file path and name. It's important to note that when the **Project_Open** subroutine is called, the HEC-RAS software starts up with the specified HEC-RAS project, but it remains open in the background. You won't see it on the Windows® desktop or on the task bar. The only way to verify that HEC-RAS is open is to view the Windows® Task Manager and see if it is present in the list of current applications. To see the HEC-RAS software during run-time, an additional line of code

```
RC.ShowRAS
```

must be added after the **Project_Open** subroutine is called. This will open HEC-RAS with the specified project, just as if it had been opened manually by double-clicking on the desktop icon.

Be aware that abnormally long path names for HEC-RAS files can cause trouble when using the HECRASController. This frequently occurs when using the default location for the HEC-RAS example projects in the C:\Program Files (x86)\HEC\HEC-RAS\[version]\Example Projects folder. Just be aware that if problems are encountered with HEC-RAS accessing files during run-time, it is possible that the path is too long. Moving all of the project files to a higher order folder (i.e. closer to the root drive C:\) might fix the problem.

Once open, the project can be executed by calling one of the "Compute" subroutines. The **Compute_CurrentPlan** subroutine requires a **Long** variable argument for the number of messages and a String array for the messages themselves. These will be populated by the **Compute_CurrentPlan** subroutine-simply provide empty variables to be populated. At this point, the code will look something like the following sample. Notice again that underscores are used to break commands over multiple lines. In addition to breaking up commentary, the underscore is used in this sample to break up a long String value that populates the **strRASProject** string. Breaking up a string within quotations requires an ampersand (&) before the underscore as shown.

```
Sub GetWSELandVelocity()
```

```
'Instantiate a new RAS500.HECRASController Class
Dim RC As New RAS500.HECRASController

'Specify the HEC-RAS project, open it, execute it.
Dim strRASProject As String 'The path and filename of the _
    desired HEC-RAS Project
Dim lngMessages As Long 'number of messages returned by _
    the HECRASController
Dim strMessages() As String 'an array of messages _
    returned by the HECRASController

strRASProject = "C:\AutomateHECRAS\Steady Examples\" & _
    "BEAVCREK.prj"
RC.Project_Open strRASProject
RC.ShowRAS
RC.Compute_CurrentPlan lngMessages, strMessages()

End Sub
```

Populating the Geometry

The next step is to ask the HECRASController for the number of river stations in the project, their names, and node types by using the **Geometry_GetNodes** subroutine. The **Geometry_GetNodes** subroutine requests five arguments, the river ID, the reach ID, the number of nodes, an array of river stations (nodes) and an array of node types. The two arrays are reference parameters meaning the RAS Controller will populate them inside the **Geometry_GetNodes** subroutine before sending back to the **GetWSELandVelocity** program. These five variables must first be declared before the **Geometry_GetNodes** subroutine can be called. In this example the Beaver Creek example project is used, which only has one river and one reach, so the River ID and Reach ID can both be set equal to 1.

```
strRASProject = "C:\AutomateHECRAS\Steady Examples\" & _
    "BEAVCREK.prj"
RC.Project_Open strRASProject
RC.ShowRAS
RC.Compute_CurrentPlan lngMessages, strMessages()

'Find the number of Nodes (River Stations) in the Beaver _
    Creek Example.
'Declare variables for the River ID and Reach ID.  Since _
    there is only one river and reach in the Beaver Creek _
    example, their ID's can both be hardcoded to 1.
Dim lngRiverID As Long, lngReachID As Long ' River ID and _
    Reach ID
Dim lngNum_RS As Long 'Number of nodes - HEC-RAS _
    Controller will populate.
Dim strRS() As String 'Array of names of the nodes
```

```
Dim strNodeType() As String 'Array of node type names _
    that go with the nodes

lngRiverID = 1
lngReachID = 1
RC.Geometry_GetNodes lngRiverID, lngReachID, lngNum_RS, _
    strRS(), strNodeType()
```

Retrieving Output

Once the River Stations and Node Types are set for all of the nodes, output from the HECRASController can be retrieved. But first, some variables must be declared. Two Single precision arrays must be declared to hold all of the water surface elevations and all of the velocity values. Since the number of river stations has already been determined, these arrays can be redimensioned to the number of river stations, **lngNum_RS**. Finally, in order for the HECRASController to know what variables to send back, it needs to know the ID numbers of the variables that are desired. Long variables **lngWS_ID** and **lngAvgVel_ID** are declared. The ID number for "Water Surface Elevation" is 2 and "Average Velocity for the Total Cross Section" is 23. All 268 HEC-RAS variable IDs are presented in Appendix E.

```
lngReachID = 1
RC.Geometry_GetNodes lngRiverID, lngReachID, lngNum_RS, _
    strRS(), strNodeType()

'Declare single arrays for water surface elevation and _
    Average Velocity
Dim sngWS() As Single 'Array of water surface elevations
Dim sngAvgVel() As Single 'Array of Average Velocities

'Redimension sngWS and sngAvgVel to the number of river _
    stations
ReDim sngWS(1 To lngNum_RS)
ReDim sngAvgVel(1 To lngNum_RS)

'Declare variables for the Water Surface Elevation and _
    Average Velocity IDs.
Dim lngWS_ID As Long 'The Water Surface Elevation ID is 2.
Dim lngAvgVel_ID As Long 'The Average Velocity ID for the _
    total cross section is 23.
lngWS_ID = 2
lngAvgVel_ID = 23
```

To retrieve the output, the **Output_NodeOutput** function will be used. Because it is a function, we need to set declared variables equal to it in the code: **sngWS()** and **sngAvgVel()**. The **Output_NodeOutput** function requests arguments for the river and reach IDs, the river station ID, an UPDN Boolean (setting this to "0" will get output for the upstream section at the bridge; the value is irrelevant for cross sections), the profile number, and the HEC-RAS variable ID number. In this example, profile number 3 is used and is hard-coded in the code. Since **Output_NodeOutput** can only send back one output variable for one cross section at a time, a **For-Next** loop is set up to populate the **sngWS()** and **sngAvgVel()** arrays. The **If-Then** block of code is used to discriminate against river stations that are not cross sections. Other types of river stations include: bridges, culverts, inline structures, lateral structures, and multiple openings. The Node Types that are sent back from the **Geometry_GetNodes** subroutine are String variables with two character IDs. For example, a bridge node has the Node Type "BR", and inline structure is "IS". Cross Sections, however, are sent back as empty strings, which are simply two quotation marks put together (i.e. ""). To only retrieve output for cross sections, the **If-Then** block searches for Node Types of "", and passes over the rest.

```
'Declare variables for the Water Surface Elevation and _
    Average Velocity IDs.
Dim lngWS_ID As Long 'The Water Surface Elevation ID is 2.
Dim lngAvgVel_ID As Long 'The Average Velocity ID for the _
    total cross section is 23.
lngWS_ID = 2
lngAvgVel_ID = 23

'Search for cross sections and populate the sngWS(), _
    sngAvgVel(), and sngRS() arrays
'    from the third profile, May '74 Flood.
Dim i As Long 'Index for the For-Next Loop
For i = 1 To lngNum_RS
    If strNodeType(i) = "" Then
        'Got a regular cross section.  An empty string _
            (i.e. "") denotes a cross section.
        sngWS(i) = RC.Output_NodeOutput(lngRiverID, _
            lngReachID, i, 0, 3, lngWS_ID)
        sngAvgVel(i) = RC.Output_NodeOutput(lngRiverID, _
            lngReachID, i, 0, 3, lngAvgVel_ID)
        strRS(i) = RC.Geometry.NodeRS(lngRiverID, _
            lngReachID, i)
    End If
Next i
```

Writing to a Spreadsheet

Now that the **sngWS()** and **sngAvgVel()** arrays are populated with the HEC-RAS output, a worksheet can be set up in Excel® to present the data in tabular form. To create a new sheet to write to and to fill that sheet with HEC-RAS output, use procedures within the **Windows.Application** class. These procedures form the basis for all of the tasks that can be accomplished in an Excel® spreadsheet. For example, if you want to select a cell on a spreadsheet and write a value in it, the **Windows.Application** class has procedures that will automate that task. Another way to look at it is the **Windows.Application** class is to Excel® as the HECRASController class is to HEC-RAS.

Perhaps the best way to learn the **Windows.Application** class is to record Macros in Excel®. By performing a number of tasks in an Excel® spreadsheet while recording those tasks to a macro, you will be able to see how Windows® writes the code to perform these tasks. While the example codes in this book demonstrate some of the more common and useful procedures in the **Windows.Application** class, those available procedures are extensive-much more so than the HECRASController-and beyond the scope of this book to describe in detail. Writing Macros is a skill that takes practice and is also outside the scope of this book. Fortunately, there are many books and online resources available that can provide more information.

The first step in writing the **GetWSELandVelocity** output to a spreadsheet is to create a new worksheet with a meaningful title. Using the **Windows.Application** class takes some practice. More specifically, it's important to know what *can't* be done and what will throw an exception. In this case, creating a new worksheet is simple, but if a name is given that already exists as the name of another sheet, an exception will be thrown, and the program will crash. Excel® doesn't allow two worksheets with the same name. So we must foresee this problem and account for that in the code. A simple **For-Next** loop can search through the existing worksheets and look for one that has the name we want to use-for this example, we'll use the name "RASResults". If that sheet does not exist, the code will create a new one with the name "RASResults". If it does exist, the code will simply select it-no need to create a new one. The following part of the code demonstrates this procedure.

```
        sngWS(i) = RC.Output_NodeOutput(lngRiverID, _
            lngReachID, i, 0, 3, lngWS_ID)
        sngAvgVel(i) = RC.Output_NodeOutput(lngRiverID, _
            lngReachID, i, 0, 3, lngAvgVel_ID)
        strRS(i) = RC.Geometry.NodeRS(lngRiverID, _
            lngReachID, i)
    End If
Next i

'Create a spreadsheet with Cross Sections, Water Surface _
    Elevations and Velocities.

'First check to see if the worksheet "RASResults" already _
    exists.  If not, add a new sheet and name it.
Dim blnSheetExists As Boolean 'Boolean tag to set to true _
    if a "RASResults" sheet already exists.
For i = 1 To Sheets.Count
    If Sheets(i).Name = "RASResults" Then
        blnSheetExists = True
    End If
```

```
Next i

'If "RASResults" does not exist as a sheet, we'll add it.
If blnSheetExists = False Then
    Sheets.Add
    ActiveSheet.Name = "RASResults"
End If
Sheets("RASResults").Select
```

Now that the "RASResults" sheet exists and has been selected, we can start entering data. If the "RASResults" sheet already existed it's a good idea to delete any data that may be in there already, to avoid possible overlapping of old data with new data. So before entering the data, a simple "Select all cells" and delete commands will provide a fresh worksheet. The **Cells.Select** and **Cells.Delete** in the **Windows.Application** class can take care of this task. The **Range** subclass is then used to create a header for the table. Notice how the index for a **Range** is the name of the cell on the spreadsheet. For example, **Range("A1")** is the cell in Column A and Row 1. Be sure to put quotes around the index, if the Column-Row protocol is used. String variables can also be used within the parentheses if desired. For this table, the river stations will be displayed in rows, and the variables will be listed in columns.

```
    Sheets.Add
    ActiveSheet.Name = "RASResults"
End If
Sheets("RASResults").Select

'Clear all the data so that can construct a fresh table _
    of data.
Cells.Select
Cells.Delete

'Give the sheet a title.
Range("A1").Select
ActiveCell.Value = "Results from Beaver Creek HEC-RAS " & _
    "run: May '74 Flood"

'Include the Active Plan Name
Range("A2").Select

ActiveCell.Value = GetCurrentPlanName(RC)

'Populate the table headers.
Range("A3") = "Cross Section"
Range("B3") = "WS El (ft)"
Range("C3") = "Avg Vel (ft/s)"
```

Finally, use a **For-Next** loop to cycle through all of the data in the **sngWSEL()** and **sngAvgVel()** arrays and write it to the table on the "RASResults" spreadsheet. Populating a table of indeterminate size requires the use of the **Offset** procedure in the

Windows.Application class. To begin, select the first cell in the table (the upper-left hand cell of the table-in this case "A4"). The Offset procedures will move through the table in a stepwise fashion, populating each cell individually as it cycles through the arrays. The first argument in the Offset procedure is the number of rows to offset. The second argument is the number of columns to offset. To advance across a table row one cell at a time, the row remains the same, so a value of 0 is used as the first argument. A value of 1 is used for the second argument. Once the end of the row in the table is reached, advance down one row and move back to the left side of the table to continue with output for the next river station. This requires 1 for the row offset argument and -2 for the column offset argument.

The **Round** function is used to present the data in the table with the desired number of decimal places. The **Round** function is contained in the **VBA.Math** class, which is inherently available when using VBA (i.e. no need to declare a new instance of the **VBA.Math** class). There are a lot of other useful procedures in the Math class for automating HEC-RAS. I highly recommend exploring it in the Object Explorer window. Without rounding, the entire **Single** precision floating point number will be entered into the cell, which can include up to nine decimal places-not appropriate for water surface elevations and velocities. This table will present water surface elevations rounded to two decimal places and velocities rounded to one decimal place. The first argument of the Round function is the number you wish to round, and the second is the number of decimal places you desire for that number. Notice that the **Round** function not only changes the number of decimal digits, but also converts the number to a string value. So be sure to declare string values for each output variable so that it works properly in your code.

After the table has been filled out, the **GetWSELandVelocity** subroutine is completed by writing the command **End Sub**. But note that HEC-RAS will remain open as both an application and a process unless the **QuitRas** subroutine is called. The **QuitRas** subroutine will immediately end HEC-RAS as an application in Windows®. And then once the End Sub command is executed, the ras.exe process will be halted. Without **QuitRas**, it's possible to end up with multiple instances of HEC-RAS open as either applications and/or processes in Windows®. This should be avoided. Since the **QuitRas** subroutine coupled with the **End Sub** command will abruptly close HEC-RAS without any indication, I prefer to include a message box just prior to the **QuitRas** subroutine that tells the user it is finished. To display a message box, use the **MsgBox** function from the VBA library in the **Interaction** class (the **Interaction** class is inherent in VBA, therefore it is not required to type this before **MsgBox**). The advantage of this is that run-time will pause, while the program waits for the user to acknowledge the message in the message box. While run-time is paused, the user will have the ability to look through the HEC-RAS software prior to its closing. Try running this code without the message box command and see how fast HEC-RAS opens, executes and closes. You may hardly notice! Once the user presses the OK button on the message box, run-time will resume, the **QuitRAS subroutine** and **End Sub** command will be executed, and HEC-RAS will close.

```
    Range("C3") = "Avg Vel (ft/s)"

    'Loop through the HEC-RAS results arrays and populate the _
        spreadsheet.  Water surface values are rounded to 2 _
        decimal places.  Velocities to 1 decimal place.

    'First, declare string values for conversion in the Round _
        function.
    Dim strWSEL As String, strAvgVel As String

    Range("A4").Select
    For i = 1 To lngNum_RS
        strWSEL = Round(sngWS(i), 2)
        strAvgVel = Round(sngAvgVel(i), 1)

        'Step through the table, populating it with HEC-RAS _
            output.
        If strNodeType(i) = "" Then
            ActiveCell.Value = strRS(i)
            ActiveCell.Offset(0, 1).Activate
            ActiveCell.Value = strWSEL
            ActiveCell.Offset(0, 1).Activate
            ActiveCell.Value = strAvgVel
            ActiveCell.Offset(1, -2).Activate
        End If
    Next i

    'Close HEC-RAS
    MsgBox "Done!"
    RC.QuitRAS

End Sub
```

Results

The final result is a new spreadsheet with a concise table showing computed water surface elevations and average velocities for each cross section for profile number 3, the "May '74 Flood" event, in plan 3, "Press/Weir Method : New Le, Lc". *Table 4* shows the resulting spreadsheet. Notice that there is some tidying up that can be done to the table to make it even more presentable. For example, you may wish to expand the width of the columns so that the entire text of each table header is visible. Recording a macro, and doing this manually in the spreadsheet will show the code required to automate this process in the application. Also, notice how the river stations for the interpolated cross sections (those marked with an asterisk*) are left justified in the table, while the regular river stations are right justified. That is because when populating the table, an asterisk is a non-numeric character so Excel® automatically converts that value from a **Single** precision number to a **String**. By default in Excel®, numerical values are right justified, string values are left justified. Again, recording a macro and manually justifying the interpolated river stations to the right will reveal the code that is required to automate this process in your procedure.

Table 4. Output presented in a Table using the HECRASController.

	A	B	C	D	E	F
1	Results from Beaver Creek HEC-RAS run: May '74 Flood					
2	Press/Weir Method : New Le, Lc					
3	Cross Sect	WS El (ft)	Avg Vel (ft/s)			
4	5.99	220.01	2.1			
5	5.875*	219.01	2			
6	5.76	218.49	1.5			
7	5.685*	218.27	1.5			
8	5.61	218.13	1.5			
9	5.49*	217.95	1.5			
10	5.41	217.32	1.6			
11	5.39	215.65	2.1			
12	5.24*	214.64	2.4			
13	5.13	213.33	2.8			
14	5.065*	212.54	2.4			
15	5	211.8	2.1			
16						
17						

◄ ► ... | RASResults | ⊕ ⋮ ◄

The entire code for the **GetWSELandVelocity** subroutine is shown below for convenience.

```
Sub GetWSELandVelocity()

    'Instantiate a new RAS500.HECRASController Class
    Dim RC As New RAS500.HECRASController

    'Specify the HEC-RAS project, open it, execute it.
    Dim strRASProject As String 'The path and filename of the _
        desired HEC-RAS Project
    Dim lngMessages As Long 'number of messages returned by _
        the HECRASController
    Dim strMessages() As String 'an array of messages _
        returned by the HECRASController

    strRASProject = "C:\AutomateHECRAS\Steady Examples\" & _
        "BEAVCREK.prj"
    RC.Project_Open strRASProject
    RC.ShowRAS
    RC.Compute_CurrentPlan lngMessages, strMessages()

    'Find the number of Nodes (River Stations) in the Beaver _
        Creek Example.
    'Declare variables for the River ID and Reach ID.  Since _
        there is only one river and reach in the Beaver Creek _
        example, their ID's can both be hardcoded to 1.
    Dim lngRiverID As Long, lngReachID As Long ' River ID and _
        Reach ID
    Dim lngNum_RS As Long 'Number of nodes - HEC-RAS _
        Controller will populate.
    Dim strRS() As String 'Array of names of the nodes
    Dim strNodeType() As String 'Array of node type names _
        that go with the nodes

    lngRiverID = 1
    lngReachID = 1
    RC.Geometry_GetNodes lngRiverID, lngReachID, lngNum_RS, _
        strRS(), strNodeType()

    'Declare single arrays for water surface elevation and _
        Average Velocity
    Dim sngWS() As Single 'Array of water surface elevations
    Dim sngAvgVel() As Single 'Array of Average Velocities

    'Redimension sngWS and sngAvgVel to the number of river _
        stations
    ReDim sngWS(1 To lngNum_RS)
    ReDim sngAvgVel(1 To lngNum_RS)

    'Declare variables for the Water Surface Elevation and _
        Average Velocity IDs.
    Dim lngWS_ID As Long 'The Water Surface Elevation ID is 2.
    Dim lngAvgVel_ID As Long 'The Average Velocity ID for the _
        total cross section is 23.
    lngWS_ID = 2
    lngAvgVel_ID = 23

    'Search for cross sections and populate the sngWS(), _
```

```
                    sngAvgVel(), and sngRS() arrays
'    from the third profile, May '74 Flood.
Dim i As Long 'Index for the For-Next Loop
For i = 1 To lngNum_RS
    If strNodeType(i) = "" Then
        'Got a regular cross section.  An empty string _
            (i.e. "") denotes a cross section.
        sngWS(i) = RC.Output_NodeOutput(lngRiverID, _
            lngReachID, i, 0, 3, lngWS_ID)
        sngAvgVel(i) = RC.Output_NodeOutput(lngRiverID, _
            lngReachID, i, 0, 3, lngAvgVel_ID)
        strRS(i) = RC.Geometry.NodeRS(lngRiverID, _
            lngReachID, i)
    End If
Next i

'Create a spreadsheet with Cross Sections, Water Surface _
    Elevations and Velocities.

'First check to see if the worksheet "RASResults" already _
    exists.  If not, add a new sheet and name it.
Dim blnSheetExists As Boolean 'Boolean tag to set to true _
    if a "RASResults" sheet already exists.
For i = 1 To Sheets.Count
    If Sheets(i).Name = "RASResults" Then
        blnSheetExists = True
    End If
Next i

'If "RASResults" does not exist as a sheet, we'll add it.
If blnSheetExists = False Then
    Sheets.Add
    ActiveSheet.Name = "RASResults"
End If
Sheets("RASResults").Select

'Clear all the data so that can construct a fresh table _
    of data.
Cells.Select
Cells.Delete

'Give the sheet a title.
Range("A1").Select
ActiveCell.Value = "Results from Beaver Creek HEC-RAS " & _
    "run: May '74 Flood"

'Include the Active Plan Name
Range("A2").Select

ActiveCell.Value = GetCurrentPlanName(RC)

'Populate the table headers.
Range("A3") = "Cross Section"
Range("B3") = "WS El (ft)"
Range("C3") = "Avg Vel (ft/s)"
```

```
'Loop through the HEC-RAS results arrays and populate the _
    spreadsheet.  Water surface values are rounded to 2 _
    decimal places.  Velocities to 1 decimal place.

'First, declare string values for conversion in the Round _
    function.
Dim strWSEL As String, strAvgVel As String

Range("A4").Select
For i = 1 To lngNum_RS
    strWSEL = Round(sngWS(i), 2)
    strAvgVel = Round(sngAvgVel(i), 1)

    'Step through the table, populating it with HEC-RAS _
        output.
    If strNodeType(i) = "" Then
        ActiveCell.Value = strRS(i)
        ActiveCell.Offset(0, 1).Activate
        ActiveCell.Value = strWSEL
        ActiveCell.Offset(0, 1).Activate
        ActiveCell.Value = strAvgVel
        ActiveCell.Offset(1, -2).Activate
    End If
Next i

'Close HEC-RAS
MsgBox "Done!"
RC.QuitRAS

End Sub
```

4

READING AND WRITING HEC-RAS INPUT FILES

As convenient and expansive as the HECRASController is, there are times where it just does not have the subroutine or function needed to accomplish a specific task. Fortunately, HEC-RAS input files are stored as ASCII (American Standard Code for Information Interchange) text files, meaning they can be opened and edited in any text editor software application (Microsoft® Word, Microsoft® WordPad, Microsoft® NotePad, etc.). Furthermore, this allows us to read and write HEC-RAS input files using built-in statements in the Visual Basic® programming language such as **Open**, and **Line Input**. In order to effectively read and write HEC-RAS input files, it's necessary to understand the structure in which these input files are built. The most common HEC-RAS input text files for reading from and writing to are:

- Geometry File, *.g##

- Steady Flow File, *.f##

- Unsteady Flow File, *.u##

Other text input files that users may wish to manipulate are:

- Plan File, *.p##

- Project File, .*prj

- Geometry Import File, *.RASImport.sdf

This chapter will cover the concepts and tools needed for reading and writing to HEC-RAS input text files. Appendices B, C, and D present the keys and their corresponding input values for the geometry, steady flow, and unsteady flow text files, respectively.

HEC-RAS Input Files

Open an HEC-RAS geometry file in a text editor and you'll immediately see a lot of text and numbers that may or may not make sense. Further inspection reveals some semblance of order, although not as easy to understand and navigate as the HEC-RAS GUI itself. However, once deciphered, you will notice that every bit of geometry input data that you can see in the HEC-RAS GUI also resides in this text file. For example, the first line in a geometry text file is "GEOM Title=XYZ", XYZ being the title of the geometry file. If you open up the Beaver Creek "Single Bridge-Example 2" Sample Problem (C:\Program Files (x86)\HEC\HEC-RAS\4.1.0\Example Projects\Steady Examples\BEAVCREK.g01), you'll see that the first line of text in the geometry text file is "GEOM Title=Beaver Cr. + Bridge - P/W".

Scanning through the geometry file, notice that most of the lines include some text followed by an equal sign (=), followed by some numbers or some text (or both). Typically, the text to the left of the equal sign is a "key"-an identifier for HEC-RAS to recognize what type of data is present on the right side of the equal sign. The data on the right side of the equal sign can be numerical, strings, dates, etc. Frequently there are multiple values to the right of the equal sign, in which case the data will be separated by a comma (comma delimited). Not all lines use comma delimitation. Some separate their input data into fields of constant spaces. This is a common input data format for older DOS-based programs like HEC-2 and HEC-6, where fields of eight spaces are used. Every input value must be segregated into a "Field of 8". The subroutine that reads the text file will then know where to delimit the input values-every eighth space. A disadvantage to this practice is the fact that every number is limited to eight digits, or seven digits and a decimal point. If more precision is needed, you are out of luck. However, HEC-RAS, when it does use field delimitation, will use fields of 16 as well, when input parameters may need more precision than that afforded by an eight digit number.

The good news for us, as programmers wishing to access these text files in a programming environment, is that if we can figure out what the key on a given line of text means, then we know what the succeeding data is. This allows us to retrieve and store any geometry data present in the geometry file if we can decipher the keys. Well, you're in luck! The geometry and flow files are deciphered in Appendices B, C, and D.

Reading HEC-RAS Input Files

Reading an HEC-RAS text file is actually very simple, once you know some key statements and a few of the text reading procedures available in VBA. It involves advancing through the text file, line by line, reading the key, and then storing the data to the right of the key to variables or structures of variables. If the user is only interested in certain geometry components, then it's only necessary to search on those components and bypass everything else. However, if desired, it is conceivable to read and store every bit of geometric data in a structure of VBA types, to be retrieved and used however you like in your program. At a rudimentary level, reading an HEC-RAS text file consists of the following lines of code:

1. A string definition set to the name of the HEC-RAS text file.

2. An **Open For Input** statement to instruct VBA to open the HEC-RAS text file.

3. A **Do Loop**, for searching through the text file, one key at a time.

4. A **Line Input** statement, which instructs VBA to read the next line in the text file and store it as some string value that can be accessed.

5. An **If Then** conditional, for locating a specific key and saving the input data into a variable.

6. A **Close** statement, which instructs VBA to close the text file.

A very simple example of reading from an HEC-RAS text file is demonstrated next. This particular piece of code searches for the title of the geometry file, and stores it into a variable.

```
Sub GetGeometryTitle()

    'Open the geometry text file to read
    Dim strGeomFile As String
    strGeomFile = "C:\AutomateHECRAS\Steady Examples\" & _
        "BEAVCREK.g01"
    Open strGeomFile For Input As #1

    'Search the geometry text file for the key "Geom Title"
    Dim strTextLine As String
    Dim strGeometryTitle As String
    Do While Not EOF(1)
        Line Input #1, strTextLine
        If InStr(strTextLine, "Geom Title") Then
            strGeometryTitle = TrimEqBefore(strTextLine)
        End If
    Loop

    'Close the text file
```

```
    Close #1

    'Message the User
    MsgBox "The Title of the geometry file is " & _
        strGeometryTitle & "."

End Sub
```

Trimming and Parsing

Notice that inside the **If Then** conditional, a function **TrimEqBefore** is called. This particular function is very useful, in fact necessary, to read HEC-RAS input text files. The equal sign (=) that HEC-RAS uses to separate the key from the input data makes parsing out the input data very easy. All we have to do is identify the position of the equal sign, and then take everything to the right of it as input data. Let's take the line of data we searched for in the example code above:

Geom Title=Beaver Cr. + Bridge - P/W

"Geom Title" is the key. We search on that key if we want to retrieve the name of the geometry file, which in this case is "Beaver Cr. + Bridge – P/W". The equal sign separates the key from the input data. The function **TrimEqBefore** removes the equal sign and everything to the left of it, leaving only the input data. String manipulation procedures like **TrimEqBefore** will be very useful in reading HEC-RAS input files. Over time, you'll build a library of your own string manipulation procedures. The **TrimEqBefore** function is shown here for your reference:

```
Public Function TrimEqBefore(x As String) As String

    'This function takes a string and trims the equal sign _
        and everything before it.

    Dim position As Long
    position = InStr(1, x, "=")
    TrimEqBefore = Right(x, Len(x) - position)

End Function
```

Many of the input keys in an HEC-RAS geometry or text file contain multiple input values. For example, the "Type RM Length L Ch R" key contains five input values after the equal sign, all separated by a comma (comma delimited). The key generally provides a good hint as to what type of data follows (but not always!) and this particular key is no exception. As the key implies, the first input data is the node type, the second is the river station for that node, the third is the left overbank reach length, fourth is main channel reach length, fifth is the right overbank reach length. Having a ready-made parsing procedure makes reading and storing this data much easier (than rewriting a parsing procedure for every read/store of input data). Two parsing procedures that will make life much easier when reading HEC-RAS geometry files are presented next. The first parsing procedure shown below is a function called **ParseString**. As its name implies, it reads and parses a comma delimited string. A referenced subroutine (**FindCommas**) provides the number and positions of the commas in the input line. These simple, yet elegant procedures were written by Mark Jensen in the early days of HEC-RAS development. To date, they are a staple of the HEC-RAS code; every time a geometry file is opened, these procedures are called multiple times (once for every comma delimited line in the geometry file).

```
Function ParseString(ByVal DataLine As String, ByRef Part() _
    As String) As Long

    'This function parses a comma delimited string variable _
        into multiple strings.

    'Written by Mark Jensen
    'Aug 19, 1993

    Dim pos() As Long
    Dim i, NumComma As Long

    ReDim pos(1000), Part(1000)
    FindCommas DataLine, pos, NumComma

    '   Get data between commas
    For i = 1 To NumComma
        Part(i) = Mid(DataLine, pos(i - 1) + 1, pos(i) - _
            pos(i - 1) - 1)
    Next i
    Part(i) = Right(DataLine, Len(DataLine) - pos(NumComma))

    '   Return the number of things found
    ParseString = NumComma + 1
End Function


Sub FindCommas(ByVal strg As String, ByRef pos() As Long, _
    ByRef num As Long)

    'This subroutine locates the commas in an input string. _
        The number of commas found is returned in the num& _
        variable and the location of the commas is stored in _
        the Pos&() array.

    'Written by Mark Jensen
    'Aug 3, 1993

    Dim i As Long
    num = 0
    For i = 1 To Len(strg)
        If Mid(strg, i, 1) = "," Then
```

```
            num = num + 1
            pos(num) = i
        End If
    Next i

End Sub
```

The next parsing procedure parses out data from a line of data in a text file that is segregated into fields of eight character positions.

```
Function ParseStringbyEights(ByVal DataLine As String, _
    ByRef Part() As String) As Long

    'This function parses an eight character string _
        delimited string variable into multiple strings.

    Dim pos() As Long
    Dim i, nParts As Long
    nParts = Len(DataLine) / 8

    ReDim pos(nParts), Part(nParts)
    For i = 0 To nParts - 1
        pos(i) = (8 * i) + 1
    Next

    'Get data for every eight spaces
    For i = 0 To nParts - 1
        Part(i) = Mid(DataLine, pos(i), 8)
    Next i

    'Return the number of things found
    ParseStringbyEights = nParts

End Function
```

There are some procedures built into the VBA library that are present in the preceding code snippets that prove very useful in manipulating strings while reading and storing data.

- **Mid(x, y, z):** This function returns a partial string from the original string, x. The partial string begins at character position y in the original string and is z positions long.

- **Right(x, y):** This function returns a partial string from the original string, x. The partial string includes all characters to the right of the y character position.

- **Len(x):** This function returns the length of string x (i.e. number of characters including spaces).

There are many more string manipulation routines built into the VBA library that may prove useful in constructing code to read and write geometry files. They generally reside in the **VBA.Strings** namespace in VBA.

Editing the Geometry Input File

Once you have become familiar with the input file construct used by HEC-RAS, writing (or rewriting) input files is easy. It really boils down to knowing the keys, and exactly how HEC-RAS expects the succeeding data to be structured (both in order and by delimitation type). In essence, you will be rebuilding the input file by copying and pasting the original input file, line by line, into a new text file. When there is a data type that changes, instead of copying from the original text file, rewrite it to the same structure, substituting any new input data for the old. The following simple subroutine demonstrates how to get into an HEC-RAS geometry file, locate the key for the geometry title, and then change the geometry title to something different. After defining the variables that will be used in this subroutine, the new geometry file is set to "Beaver Creek Example Project". The standard comment header that I use for my code to provide some basic (and useful!) information about the code is included. The first comment briefly describes what the procedure does. The second comment includes the author and date. The third comment provides more detail about the code, including important notes and comments that someone inheriting the code would want to know. The final comment indicates what the code was tested with.

```vba
Sub ChangeGeometryTitle()

    '***********************************************************
    'Demonstrates how to read and write to an HEC-RAS text _
        file.

    'Written by Christopher Goodell
    'Oct 27, 2013

    'This subroutine reads the geometry input file, finds the _
        geometry title key, and replaces the original _
        geometry title with a new title.

    'Tested with the BEAVCREK.g01 geometry file.
    '***********************************************************

    'Define the new geometry title to use.
    Dim strNewGeometryTitle As String
    strNewGeometryTitle = "Beaver Creek Example Project"

    'Define the read and write files.
    Dim strReadFileName As String
    Dim strWriteFileName As String
```

```
    strReadFileName = "C:\AutomateHECRAS\Steady Examples\" & _
        "BEAVCREK.g01"
    strWriteFileName = "C:\AutomateHECRAS\Steady Examples\" & _
        "BEAVCREK.g01temp"

    'Open the read and write files input (reading) and _
        output (writing)
    Open strReadFileName For Input As #1
    Open strWriteFileName For Output As #2

    'Search for the key "Geom Title".  When found, change the _
        title then close the read and write files.
    Dim strTextLine As String
    Do While Not EOF(1)
        Line Input #1, strTextLine
        If InStr(1, strTextLine, "Geom Title") Then
            Print #2, "Geom Title=" & strNewGeometryTitle
        Else
            Print #2, strTextLine
        End If
    Loop
    Close #1
    Close #2

    'Replace the original geometry file with the temporary _
        one, then delete the temporary one.
    FileCopy strWriteFileName, strReadFileName
    Kill strWriteFileName

    'A message box to let the user know it's done.
    MsgBox "Done!  Geometry Title changed to " & _
        strNewGeometryTitle & "."

End Sub
```

Next, the geometry text file you want to read is defined. Notice that the entire file path, as well as the file name, is included in the name of the text file to read. This file must already exist prior to running this subroutine-it is created when a geometry file is first saved in an HEC-RAS project. The **Open...For Input** statement tells VBA this is a text file that it will be reading data from. The numerical ID, **#1** provides a convenient (and mandatory) way to reference that text file later on in the code.

Immediately following, a new text file is named. This will be the temporary file that the subroutine will write to. It's temporary because once it is created, it will replace the original geometry text file, taking on the original file name. This coding strategy is required since VBA does not allow reading and writing to the same text file simultaneously. In essence, you will be copying the read file, line by line, to the write file, changing only what you desire to be changed-in this example we are simply changing the title of the geometry file. The **Open...For Output** statement tells VBA this is a text file that it will write data to. This line also requires a numerical reference-**#2** in this case.

The succeeding **Do Loop** block handles the step-by-step rewrite of the original geometry text file. The **Do** statement instructs VBA to loop through this process until the end of the text file is reached (**EOF**). Inside the **Do Loop** block the **Line Input** statement advances to the next line in the read text file, and the String value, **strTextLine** is assigned that entire line of text. **strTextLine** is evaluated to determine whether it contains the key that we're searching for. The **Do Loop** is in effect searching for the line that contains the geometry file title. The title of the geometry file resides after the equals sign on the Geom Title key (see Appendix B). So once we find a line of text where any part of it includes "Geom Title", we can rewrite that line in the new text file, by using the **Print** statement, to include the new geometry file title after the key and the equal sign.

Inside the **Do Loop** block, any number of searches are possible. This example only changes the geometry title. The same **Do Loop** can be used to change anything in the geometry file, from altering Manning's n values, resizing spillways, adjusting discharge coefficients, or all three. We complete the subroutine by closing the respective text files, and then replacing the original one with the new one. This is accomplished by copying over the original geometry text file with the newly created temporary one. The **Kill** statement is then used to delete the temporary file. The geometry file will now have a new title, "Beaver Creek Example Project."

5

STRATEGIES

Navigating the Excel® Spreadsheet in Run Time

Running an application in Excel® allows the user to take advantage of the built-in functionality of the Excel® spreadsheet. This is very convenient, particularly when dealing with a lot of data that a user may eventually want to see, and possibly edit, after the application has completed. A good example is the retrieval and display of output data at a number of cross sections for multiple profiles. Think of the profile output table in HEC-RAS. Understanding how to automate the process of data retrieval from the HEC-RAS output file and how to navigate around an Excel® spreadsheet in run time, allows the user to organize and display output data in a desired format.

The most common method for moving around the spreadsheet in run time is the **Offset** property. The **Offset** property is a member of the **Excel.Range** class and returns a range object that represents an offset from a specified range. In other words, it directs VBA to move from one cell to another. This is done by specifying the row and column offset as arguments. For example, if a user wants to move from the active cell to a cell four rows down and three columns to the right, he can type the command, **ActiveCell.Offset(4,3).Activate**. **ActiveCell** is a Range property that indicates the currently occupied cell in a spreadsheet. If, for example, the active cell is cell A1, then the **ActiveCell.Offset(4,3)** is cell D5. The **Activate** method simply instructs VBA to activate the offset cell; cell D5 becomes the active cell.

The **Offset** property then becomes critical when writing a large amount of data to a spreadsheet. A **For Next** loop makes this task efficient and compact.

```
For i = 1 to lngProfile
    sngStage = RC.Output_NodeOutput(lngRivID, lngReachID, _
        lngNodeID, 1, i, 2)
    sngFlow = RC.Output_NodeOutput(lngRivID, lngReachID, _
        lngNodeID, 1, i, 9)
    sngVelocity = RC.Output_NodeOutput(lngRivID, lngReachID, _
        lngNodeID, 1, i, 25)
    ActiveCell.Value = Trim(strProfile(i))
    ActiveCell.Offset(0,1).Activate
    ActiveCell.Value = Round(sngStage,2)
    ActiveCell.Offset(0,1).Activate
    ActiveCell.Value = Round(sngFlow,2)
    ActiveCell.Offset(0,1).Activate
    ActiveCell.Value = Round(sngVelocity,2)
    ActiveCell.Offset(1,-3).Activate
Next i
```

This block of code lists out the stage, flow, and velocity for "lngNodeID". Each row in the table represents a new profile of output data. There are "lngProfile" number of profiles, in the **For Next** loop, and in each iteration, the table is built by using the

Offset property.   The **Round** function is used to keep the number of decimal places appropriate for display. After each variable is placed in a cell, the code advances one column to the right (0,1) for the next variable. After the row is complete, the code returns to the initial column and advances one row (1,-3) to begin a new profile of data. The result is an output table as shown in *Table 5*. Profile name in the first column, stage in the second, flow in the third, and velocity in the fourth.

Table 5. Creating a table using the ActiveCell.Offset Property.

	A	B	C	D
1	01JAN1999 1200	658.95	729.01	2.67
2	01JAN1999 1300	658.92	725.70	2.71
3	01JAN1999 1400	658.91	722.63	2.71
4	01JAN1999 1500	658.91	720.53	2.70
5	01JAN1999 1600	658.91	719.78	2.70
6	01JAN1999 1700	658.91	720.52	2.70
7				
8				

There are a number of other useful Excel® properties and procedures that will assist in building tables in run time:

1. Sheets(*a*): Class in Excel® library representing spreadsheet *a*. The argument, *a*, is a string value representing the name of the sheet, found on the tab of the sheet.

2. Range(*a*): Class in Excel® Library representing cell *a*. The argument, *a*, is a string value in the format "A1".

3. Range(a:b): Class in Excel® Library representing a range of cells, *a:b*. The argument, *a:b*, is a string value representing a range of cells in the format "A1:Z10".

4. Cells(a, b): Property in Application Class of the Excel® Library. Similar to **Range**, only "a" and "b" are integers (i.e. Column A is 1, column B is 2, etc.). This can provide more efficiency than **Range**, as the arguments can be referenced to the count in a For-Next loop, avoiding the repeated selection of new cells. For example, the code above using the **ActiveCell.Offset** property could be re-written using the **Cells()** property, and will perform much faster:

```
For i = 1 to lngProfile
    sngStage = RC.Output_NodeOutput(lngRivID, lngReachID, _
        lngNodeID, 1, i, 2)
    sngFlow = RC.Output_NodeOutput(lngRivID, lngReachID, _
        lngNodeID, 1, i, 9)
    sngVelocity = RC.Output_NodeOutput(lngRivID, _
        lngReachID, lngNodeID, 1, i, 25)
    Cells(i, 1).Value = Trim(strProfile(i))
    Cells(i, 2).Value = Round(sngStage,2)
    Cells(i, 3).Value = Round(sngFlow,2)
    Cells(i, 4).Value = Round(sngVelocity,2)
Next i
```

5. Select: Function in the Range class of the Excel® Library. Selects a cell or range of cells.

6. Activate: Method in the Range class of the Excel® Library. Activates a single cell within a selected range.

7. ActiveCell: Property in the Application class of the Excel® Library. Indicates the currently active cell inside the current selection.

8. Value: Property in the Range class of the Excel® Library. Used to enter a value into a cell or to query the value in a cell.

9. Selection: Property in the Application class of the Excel® Library.

10. Clear: Function in the Range class of the Excel® Library. Used to delete the content and formatting for a range of cells.

11. ClearContents: Function in the Range class of the Excel® Library. Used to delete the contents in a range of cells.

12. Delete: Function in the Range class of the Excel® Library. Used to delete a range of cells.

Keeping Track of Progress

For an application that takes some time to perform tasks, it may be desirable to monitor the progress of the application while it's running. While VBA is plodding through a particularly complex loop (**For Next**, **Do Loop**, etc.) that performs a number of computations, the user may not see anything happen for a while, which can be disconcerting. "Did the program crash? Is it stuck in a loop?" It may just be that there is a lot of work going on and the program takes some time to finish. Either way, providing feedback during the run, indicating some form of progress, can set the user at ease with the knowledge that the program is humming along nicely. There are a number of ways in VBA to provide feedback on progress during a run. I'll discuss three ways to do this. Any one of these (or all of them) can be used to indicate progress.

The "Wait" Cursor

By default, the cursor on your screen, when in Excel®, looks like an arrow, pointing up and to the left (the Northwest Arrow):   But, when you hover over an Excel® spreadsheet, it looks like a hollow cross, or one of the familiar shapes in the old Tetris® game. Anywhere you can add text, Excel® will change the cursor automatically to the I Beam. However, when things are happening in the background, you may have noticed that Windows® will change the cursor to "Busy", a rotating circle, to let you know to be patient...things are happening in the background. Once the cursor changes back to a hollow cross, you're ready to resume whatever task you were working on. The "Busy" cursor can be incorporated into your VBA applications and it's a good idea to do this for any application that takes more than a few seconds to run.

The cursor object resides in the **Windows.Application** class. There are four cursor properties the **Excel.MousePointer** class that the cursor can be set to:

- xlDefault. Whatever the default is for a location in Excel®. For example, on the spreadsheet, you get the hollow cross. In a text box, you get the IBeam. In the Menu area, you get the Northwest Arrow. These are automatically changed as you move the cursor around, when you are in default mode.

- xlIBeam. The I-beam shape commonly used in word processors. The cursor will remain the IBeam no matter where you hover in Excel®.

- xlNorthwestArrow. The familiar arrow pointing up and to the left. The cursor will remain the IBeam no matter where you hover in Excel®.

- xlWait. The rotating circle; the "Busy" cursor. The cursor will remain the rotating circle no matter where you hover in Excel®.

I generally use xlWait (the rotating circle) while the program is running, and xlDefault once the program has finished. The following is an example of the use of the cursor object.

```
Sub OpenRASProject()

    '*************************************************************
    'Demonstrates Project_Open subroutine and the cursor _
        property.

    'Written by Christopher Goodell
```

```
'July 31, 2012

'Opens a RAS project by being called from another _
    subroutine
'*************************************************************

'Change the cursor to the Rotating Circle
Application.Cursor = xlWait

'Open a RAS Project
Dim RC As New RAS500.HECRASController
Dim strFilename As String
Sheets("RASProjects").Select
strFilename = Range("C4").Value
RC.Project_Open strFilename 'First open the RAS project
RC.ShowRAS
MsgBox "The HEC-RAS project " & strFilename & " is open."

'Change the cursor back to default.
Application.Cursor = xlDefault

'Close HEC-RAS
RC.QuitRAS

End Sub
```

The Status Bar

At times, it may be useful to provide more information to the user than just the "wait" cursor, while an application is working in the background. The rotating circle indicates that something is happening in the background, but you really don't know the degree of progress being made, or if indeed the program is stuck in a loop. The Status Bar provides a convenient method for communicating information about progress to the user during run time so that the user can know how computations are proceeding. Perhaps more importantly, it can let the user know if there is enough time to get a cup of coffee, before the program finishes.

The Status Bar is located on the bottom of the Excel® worksheet, just below the sheet tabs (with the default settings), as shown in Figure 17. In this example, all of the plans of an HEC-RAS project are being run, sequentially. The name of the plan currently being run, "Sunny Day Failure", is written to the Status Bar.

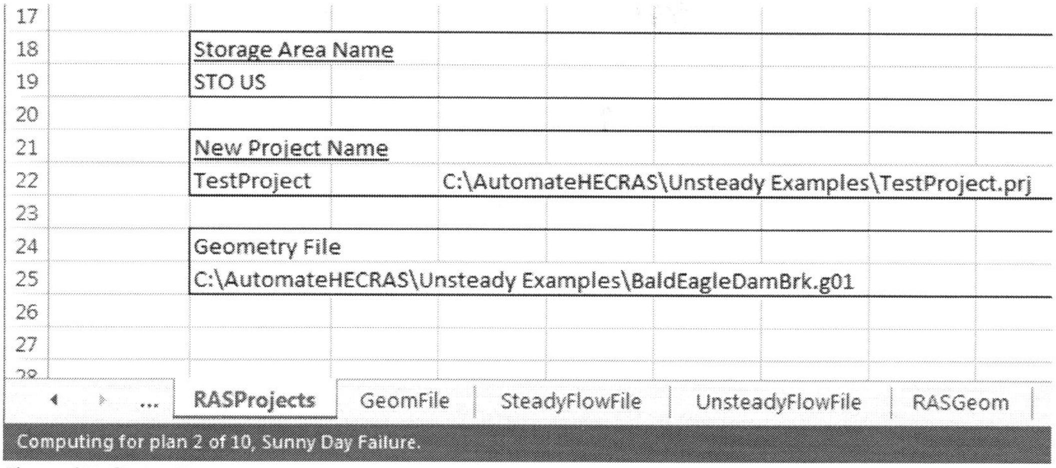

17						
18	Storage Area Name					
19	STO US					
20						
21	New Project Name					
22	TestProject		C:\AutomateHECRAS\Unsteady Examples\TestProject.prj			
23						
24	Geometry File					
25	C:\AutomateHECRAS\Unsteady Examples\BaldEagleDamBrk.g01					
26						
27						
28						

◄ ► ...	RASProjects	GeomFile	SteadyFlowFile	UnsteadyFlowFile	RASGeom

Computing for plan 2 of 10, Sunny Day Failure.

Figure 17. Status Bar.

The programmer can insert lines of code specifying the text to be written to the status bar that will let the user know periodically what is happening while the program is running. In the following sample code, the subroutine cycles through a **For Next** loop for the number of plans in the Bald Eagle Dam Break example project. For each plan, it instructs HEC-RAS to set that plan to current, and then compute the current plan. Just prior to calling the **Compute_CurrentPlan** function, the subroutine writes a message to the Status Bar, so the user can see which plan is being computed during run time.

```
Sub StatusBarExample()

    '*******************************************************
    'Demonstrates the Excel Status Bar.

    'Written by Christopher Goodell
    'December 10, 2013

    'Runs through a series of plans and shows the progress _
        using a status bar.  Returns the status bar to the _
        previous message.

    'Tested with the FLODENCR.prj data set.
    '*******************************************************

    'Open a RAS project
    Dim RC As New RAS500.HECRASController
    Dim strFilename As String
    Sheets("RASProjects").Select
    strFilename = Range("C4").Value
    RC.Project_Open strFilename

    'Get the plan names
    Dim lngPlanCount As Long, strPlanNames() As String
    Dim blnIncludeBasePlansOnly As Boolean
    blnIncludeBasePlansOnly = True
    RC.Plan_Names lngPlanCount, strPlanNames(), _
```

61

```
            blnIncludeBasePlansOnly

    'Remember current Status Bar settings and set the display
    '    property to True
    Dim blnOldStatusBar As Boolean
    blnOldStatusBar = Application.DisplayStatusBar
    Application.DisplayStatusBar = True

    'Loop through all the plans and compute each one, sending _
        a message to the status bar.
    Dim blnDidItCompute As Boolean, lngNMsg As Long, strMsg() _
        As String
    Dim i As Integer
    For i = 1 To lngPlanCount
        RC.Plan_SetCurrent (strPlanNames(i))
        'Write the current plan to the Status Bar
        Application.StatusBar = "Computing for plan " _
        & i & " of " & lngPlanCount & ", " & strPlanNames(i) _
            & "."
        blnDidItCompute = RC.Compute_CurrentPlan(lngNMsg, _
            strMsg())
    Next i

    'Reset Status Bar to previous settings
    Application.StatusBar = False
    Application.DisplayStatusBar = blnOldStatusBar

    'Close HEC-RAS
    RC.QuitRAS

End Sub
```

It's always a good idea to not only present what is happening at the moment, but to also indicate some degree of progress. The example in Figure 17 lists the current plan, but also indicates which plan number, out of the total number of plans, the application is working on.

This strategy gives the user some idea of how far along the program is in its task of running all of the plans. The Status Bar is a property in the **Windows.Application** Class. Keep in mind that the Status Bar property is set to Excel®, not to the specific Excel® workbook you have open. Therefore, whatever message is in the status bar, will remain there even if you open a new, completely unrelated workbook. So make sure you write some code that will return the Status Bar to its previous setting. In the example code above, prior to writing anything to the Status Bar, the subroutine stores the Status Bar Display settings in a **Boolean** variable. Then after all of the HEC-RAS Plans are run, the Status Bar text is erased, by setting **Application.StatusBar** to False, and then its display status is returned to the original setting.

The Progress Bar

Another way to demonstrate progress during run-time is with a progress bar. Because a progress bar is an object that must be added, it requires a little more effort beyond the cursor and status bar options, but can add a nice look to your application and provide a very quick, easy-to-gauge reading of its progress. Excel® comes with a number of form controls that can serve as objects. Each of these controls is a class in itself, and therefore comes with a number of built-in properties that can be set either prior to, or during run time. Controls are useful for providing the user an interactive way to control a software program. They are the basis behind object-oriented programming. In fact, all of the commands on the Excel® Quick Access Toolbar are controls, mostly of the class "Buttons".

To use a progress bar, we'll have to create a new form in the VBA workspace. Until now, we've been writing code, but in the VBA workspace a graphical form can be added by right clicking anywhere in the Project Explorer viewer, and selecting Insert...UserForm. You'll see a new folder added in the Project Explorer called "Forms" with a new form in it called "UserForm1". The form is added to the VBA Workspace as a gridded canvas to create your object-oriented artwork.

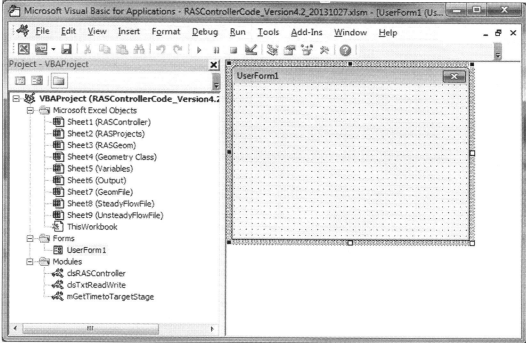

Figure 18. Adding a New Form.

From here, you can add controls and develop your own utility with a "stand-alone" feel to it, without any interaction with the spreadsheet in Excel®. The available controls are shown in the toolbox by selecting the toolbox icon in the VBA workspace or by going to View...Toolbox.

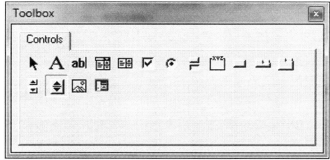

Figure 19. VBA Toolbox of Controls.

There are a little more than a dozen controls already in the toolbox, but by right-clicking anywhere on the Control tab in the toolbox, you can find additional controls-and there are many already loaded to your computer. To show progress, we need to add a progress bar to the tool box. Fortunately, there is a progress bar available in "Additional Controls". Scroll down to Microsoft ProgressBar Control (or any other Progress Bar Control that may be in your Additional Controls library). Check the box next to it and click OK. This will add a progress bar to your list of controls in the tool box.

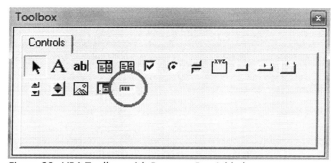

Figure 20. VBA Toolbox with Progress Bar Added.

Clicking the ProgressBar tool will allow you to draw a progress bar onto your form. For this example, all that is needed on the form is the progress bar. So the form can be sized down to fit only the progress bar-for a nice streamlined look. The name of both the form and the progress bar should also be changed to something more meaningful than the default names. When naming objects, the programming convention is to give the name a prefix that indicates what kind of object it is, followed by a descriptive name. I've found this to be very useful, especially when trying to interpret old code. In this example, I've called the form, "frmProg" and the progress bar "progProg".

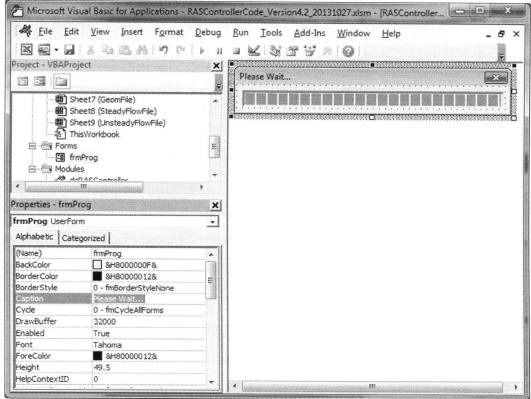

Figure 21. New form with Progress Bar.

The names (and other properties of the objects) can be viewed and edited on the Properties Window (View…Properties Window). The following code demonstrates the progress bar.

```
Sub ProgressBarExample()
    '******************************************************
    'Demonstrates the use of a Progress Bar

    'Written by Christopher Goodell
    'December 10, 2013

    'Runs through a series of plans and shows the progress _
        using a progress bar

    'Tested with the FLODENCR.prj data set.
    '******************************************************
```

```
'Open an HEC-RAS project
Dim RC As New RAS500.HECRASController
Dim strFilename As String
Sheets("RASProjects").Select
strFilename = Range("C4").Value
RC.Project_Open strFilename

'Get an array of Plan Names
Dim lngPlanCount As Long, strPlanNames() As String
Dim blnIncludeBasePlansOnly As Boolean
blnIncludeBasePlansOnly = True
RC.Plan_Names lngPlanCount, strPlanNames(), _
    blnIncludeBasePlansOnly

'Set properties on the Progress form, and Show it.
Dim frmProg As New frmProg
frmProg.progProg.Min = 0
frmProg.progProg.Max = 100
frmProg.progProg.Value = 0
frmProg.Show (False)

'Cycle through the plans and compute each one,
'    changing the progress bar value each time.
Dim blnDidItCompute As Boolean, lngNMsg As Long, strMsg() _
    As String
Dim i As Integer
For i = 1 To lngPlanCount
    RC.Plan_SetCurrent (strPlanNames(i))
    RC.Compute_HideComputationWindow
    blnDidItCompute = RC.Compute_CurrentPlan(lngNMsg, _
        strMsg())
    frmProg.progProg.Value = (i / lngPlanCount) * 100
Next i

'Close HEC-RAS
frmProg.Caption = "Finished!"
RC.QuitRAS

End Sub
```

Notice the caption for the form has been changed in the Properties Window to "Please Wait…" To use the new progress form, declare it as a new variable in the code and "show" it. Make sure to set the Modal argument for the **Show** event to "False". When a form is shown and set to Modal, it maintains priority and the subroutine is paused until that form is closed. By setting it to Modeless, VBA will continue to progress through the subroutine, even with the form "shown." The actual progress displayed on the progress bar during run time is set in its "Value" property, as well as defining a minimum and maximum numerical value for progress.

Progress Using Events

Event programming is a convenient way to have control over your application during run-time. A typical application without events will run from start to finish, calling procedures along the way as they are written, with no interaction from the user during run-time.   One of the most commonly-used HECRASController procedures is the **Compute_CurrentPlan** subroutine. Once computations are initiated with the **Compute_CurrentPlan** subroutine, run-time is paused while HEC-RAS runs through its simulation. Only when the simulation is complete, will VBA resume run-time and proceed through the rest of the code. Let's say the programmer wishes to provide some information to the user during the HEC-RAS computations. This can be accomplished two ways: through event programming or by setting the **Compute_CurrentPlan** parameter "BlockingMode" to False.   Event programming provides a method for the user to fire off procedures while another procedure is working. Setting BlockingMode to False tells VBA to continue on with the current procedure, even while HEC-RAS is running. There is a reason that BlockingMode is set to True, by default. You could get into trouble if your code tries to access HEC-RAS output while HEC-RAS is simulating. So it's a good idea to be careful by setting BlockingMode to false when calling the **Compute_CurrentPlan** function.

In HEC-RAS Version 5.0, the HECRASController has two events: **ComputeProgressBar**, and **ComputeProgressMessage**.   As the names suggest, these two events will provide information about the HEC-RAS computations to the user while HEC-RAS is computing.   The previous section demonstrates how to use a progress bar to inform the user of the progress of opening a series of plans and running each one successively. The two HECRASController events return progress information specifically for the HEC-RAS computations alone. **ComputeProgressBar** returns a single value called "Progress", a number between 0 and 1 that indicates the level of progress of the HEC-RAS computations. A value of 0 means computations have yet to begin, a value of 1 indicates computations have completed. **ComputeProgressMessage** returns string values that replicate the messages you see in the HEC-RAS computation window during the simulation.   Both progress and progress messages are available to the user through the HEC-RAS Computation window, so the two available events in the HECRASController are redundant, provided the application does not hide the computation window (**Compute_HideComputationWindow**). However, if the user wishes to keep the computation window hidden, but still provide computation progress to the user, the HECRASController events can be used.

Though Version 5.0 is limited to two specific events in the HECRASController, a programmer can code his own events for any user action. For example, an event could be written so that when a user enters a new HEC-RAS geometry input value to a cell on a worksheet, the input value is automatically, and immediately written to the geometry text file. This would bypass the extra mouse clicks required to initiate the code through a VBA object like a command button.

Event programming in VBA requires a specific coding protocol. The class that contains the event (the HECRASController class or any other programmed class with events) must be declared in the general section of a class module or an object module (i.e. external to any subroutines or functions within that module).

To begin, first insert a new class module by right-clicking on the VBAProject icon in the Project Explorer and selecting Insert…Class Module. A new class module will be inserted into the Class Modules folder and by default will be named "Class1". Once inserted, you can rename the class to something more meaningful (Figure 22).

Before any source code is written, declare a variable as HECRASController using **Dim WithEvents**. This is placed at the top of the class, before all of the procedures (Figure 23). Note that the statement **New** is not used here when declaring a new class globally (i.e. above the source code in the class module). Therefore, the **Set** statement must be used within any procedure in the class that wishes to instantiate a new HECRASController class (for example, **Set RC = HECRASController**). The **WithEvents** keyword enables the events that are preprogrammed within the HECRASController class, so that they may be called in the code. There is already an event that comes with every class module, called **Class_Initialize()**, but we'll ignore that and work directly with the HECRASController. In the following example, we'll be using the Progress form in two different subroutines in the new **clsRASControllerEvents**, so a variable must be declared as a new **frmProg** before the source code so that it is public to all procedures in the class.

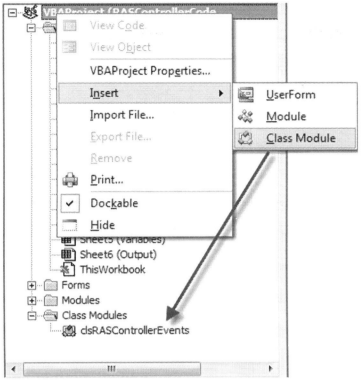

Figure 22. Insert Class Module.

Once a new HECRASController is declared with events, the declared variable (**RC** in the example) will show up in the dropdown box in the upper left above the code window. When RC is selected in the left dropdown box, you'll see the two HECRASController events automatically populated in the right dropdown box. Click on the **ComputeProgressBar** event in the right dropdown box and VBA will automatically insert a new subroutine called **RC_ComputeProgressBar()** as shown in Figure 23.

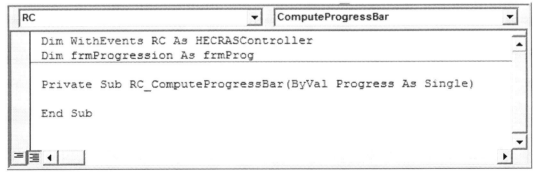

Figure 23. The ComputeProgressBar event.

Now the **ComputeProgressBar** subroutine is ready for some code. The code here is quite simple. It takes the variable **Progress**, returned by the HECRASController during computations and applies it to the progress bar. This subroutine will be pinged repeatedly throughout the computations, allowing us to show progress for the duration of the simulation.

```
Sub RC_ComputeProgressBar(ByVal Progress As Single)

    '*********************************************************
    'Demonstrates the ComputeProgressBar event in the _
        HECRASController.

    'Written by Christopher Goodell
    'April 11, 2014

    'After you declare WithEvents RC as HECRASController the _
        events in the HECRASController will show up in the _
        dropdown box in the upper right, if RC is selected in _
        the upper left dropdown box.  Sends the progress _
        value to the progress bar.
    '*********************************************************

    'To make sure we only get Progress Values between 0 and 1.
    If Progress < 0 Then Progress = 0
    If Progress > 1 Then Progress = 1

    frmProgression.progProg.Value = Progress * 100

End Sub
```

Now that the **ComputeProgressBar** subroutine is set up in the class module, a subroutine can be written in a standard module to initiate the "events". This simply requires a declaration of a variable (**clsEvnts**) as a new instance of the newly created class (**clsRASControllerEvents**).

```
Sub ComputeProgressBar()

    '*********************************************************
    'Demonstrates the ComputeProgressBar Event.

    'Written by Christopher Goodell
    'April 14, 2014

    'Calls the ComputeProgressBar event from clsEvnts.  This _
        shows how to use a progress bar during computations.

    'Tested with the BaldEagleDamBrk.prj data set.  Any _
        HEC-RAS project will work, but data sets that take a _
        long time to run will demonstrate this better.
    '*********************************************************

    'Declare a new instance of clsRASControllerEvents
    Dim clsEvnts As New clsRASControllerEvents

    'call the ComputeProgressBar event
    clsEvnts.ComputeProgressBar
End Sub
```

Figure 24 shows both the HEC-RAS computation window and the progress bar that was created in the middle of computation.

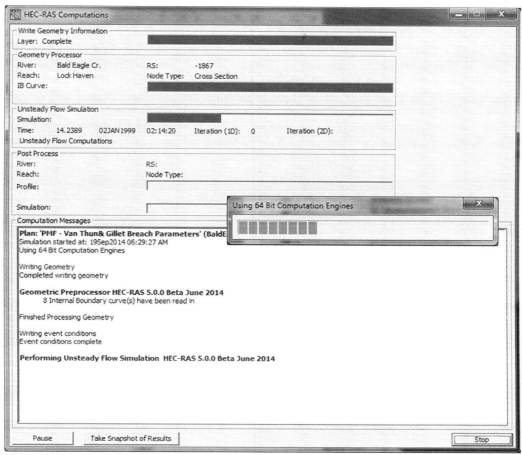

Figure 24. Progress Bar showing progress.

Progress Using BlockingMode set to False

Setting BlockingMode to False tells VBA to continue on with the current procedure, even while HEC-RAS is running. Inserting a Do-Loop after the **Compute_CurrentPlan** subroutine is called with BlockingMode set to False, provides an easy and convenient way to show the user progress. The advantage that using Events has over setting BlockingMode to False is that Events will return useful information about the status of the HEC-RAS computations. Therefore, your messages sent to the user while using BlockingMode set to False will have to be more generic; something like "Still Computing..."

There is a reason that BlockingMode is set to True, by default. You could get into trouble if your code tries to access HEC-RAS output while HEC-RAS is simulating. So it's a good idea to be careful when setting BlockingMode to false, by stepping into a controlled Do-Loop, one that will remain looping until HEC-RAS is done computing. The following code demonstrates how one might use BlockingMode set to False to show the user progress. The **Compute_Complete** function is tested for each loop to check if computations are done. While HEC-RAS is computing, the elapsed time is computed in the Do-Loop and reported to the Status Bar. **Compute_Complete** can only be called when setting BlockingMode to False.

```
Sub ComputeBlockingModeFalse()

    '*****************************************************
    'Demonstrates the Compute_CurrentPlan Function with _
        Blocking Mode set to False.

    'Written by Christopher Goodell
    'September 18, 2014

    'Computes the current plan with BlockingMode set to _
        false.  While HEC-RAS is computing, a Do-Loop will _
        keep track of progress.

    'Tested with the BaldEagleDamBrk.prj data set.  Any _
        HEC-RAS project will work, but longer running data _
        sets demonstrate the BlockingMode feature best.
    '*****************************************************

    'Instantiate a new HECRASController
    Dim RC As New RAS500.HECRASController

    'Open the Project
    Dim strFilename As String
    Sheets("RASProjects").Select
    strFilename = Range("C4").Value
    RC.Project_Open (strFilename) 'First open the RAS project

    'Compute the current plan.
    Dim lngMessages As Long
    Dim strMessages() As String
    Dim blnDidItCompute As Boolean
    Dim blnBlockingMode As Boolean

    blnBlockingMode = False
    blnDidItCompute = RC.Compute_CurrentPlan(lngMessages, _
        strMessages(), blnBlockingMode)

    'Continue to loop, checking to see if HEC-RAS has finished
    '    computing.  When done, exit the do-loop.
    Dim blnDidItComplete As Boolean
    Dim dteStart
    Dim dteElapsedTime
    dteStart = Now()
    Do
        dteElapsedTime = Now() - dteStart
        blnDidItComplete = RC.Compute_Complete()
```

```
    If blnDidItComplete = False Then
        'Report the elapsed time.
        Application.StatusBar = "Still working.  " & _
            "Elapsed Time = " & Hour(dteElapsedTime) & _
            ":" & Minute(dteElapsedTime) & _
            ":" & Second(dteElapsedTime)
    Else
        'Computations are done. Report total time to _
            complete.
        Application.StatusBar = "Finished! That " & _
            "took " & Hour(dteElapsedTime) & _
            ":" & Minute(dteElapsedTime) & _
            ":" & Second(dteElapsedTime)
    End If
Loop Until blnDidItComplete = True

    'Close HEC-RAS
    RC.QuitRAS

End Sub
```

The List Box

Using forms along with code unlocks a wide range of strategies for user interaction with your application. The progress bar was shown in the previous section to be a simple, yet effective way to communicate the progress of your application while it is running. The ListBox can show a scrolling list of messages during run-time, giving the user valuable information about the status of the computations. While the progress bar is limited to showing progress during run-time, the list box can provide limitless amounts of information to the user about what is happening in the background while the application is working. Like the progress bar, a list box is a form control available to use from the controls in the VBA toolbox.

Figure 25. ListBox form control.

Add the ListBox to a new form (**frmList**) and size it to fit the messages that will be displayed. In this example, the caption for **frmList** has been changed to "Computation Messages".

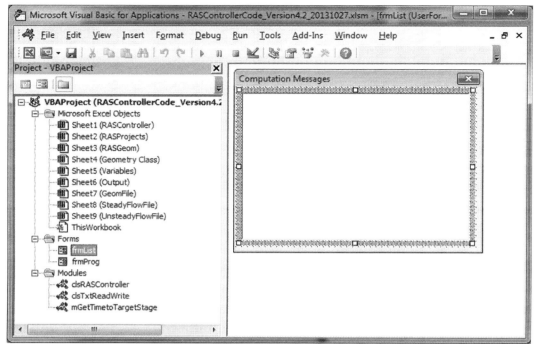

Figure 26. The VBA ListBox.

The code is similar to the Progress Bar code, only instead of changing the values for the progress bar, messages are added to the ListBox using the **.lstMessages.AddItem** method.

```
Sub ListBoxExample()

    '***********************************************************
    'Demonstrates the use of a ListBox.

    'Written by Christopher Goodell
    'December 11, 2013

    'Opens an existing HEC-RAS project, executes each plan _
        and writes a message to a list box window after each _
        plan run.

    'Tested with the BEAVCREK.prj data set.
    '***********************************************************

    'Open an HEC-RAS Project
    Dim RC As New RAS500.HECRASController
    Dim strFilename As String
    Sheets("RASProjects").Select
    strFilename = Range("C4").Value
    RC.Project_Open strFilename

    'Get a list of all of the plans
    Dim lngPlanCount As Long, strPlanNames() As String
    Dim blnIncludeBasePlansOnly As Boolean
    blnIncludeBasePlansOnly = True
```

```
    RC.Plan_Names lngPlanCount, strPlanNames(), _
        blnIncludeBasePlansOnly

    'Show the ListBox Form, frmList
    Dim frmListBox As New frmList
    frmListBox.Show (False)
    frmListBox.lstMessages.AddItem "Running HEC-RAS Plans."

    'Cycle through the plans and compute each one,
    '    adding a line of text to the ListBox each time.
    Dim i As Integer
    Dim blnDidItCompute As Boolean, lngMsg As Long, strMsg() _
        As String
    For i = 1 To lngPlanCount
        RC.Plan_SetCurrent (strPlanNames(i))
        RC.Compute_HideComputationWindow
        blnDidItCompute = RC.Compute_CurrentPlan(lngMsg, _
            strMsg())
        frmListBox.lstMessages.AddItem "Running plan " & _
            strPlanNames(i) & "."
    Next i

    frmListBox.lstMessages.AddItem "All Plans have been run."
    frmListBox.Caption = "Finished!"

    'Close HEC-RAS
    RC.QuitRAS

End Sub
```

As the subroutine **ListBoxExample** is being run, a scrolling list of messages show up, one at a time, providing the user updates on which HEC-RAS plans are being computed. When the subroutine is complete, a final message, "All Plans have been run." is displayed and the ListBox form caption is changed to "Finished!"

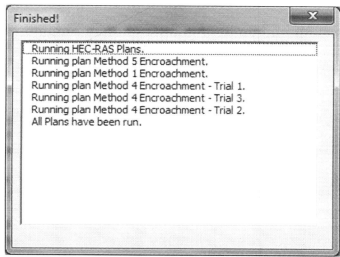

Figure 27. ListBox Computation Messages.

Error Handling

It is nearly inevitable that written code with any level of complexity will have bugs in it. A bug is an unforeseen consequence in the code that makes an application do something unexpected or unintended. It might be a user input error, like entering a 0 for an input that will be used as the denominator of an equation, causing the program to attempt to divide by 0. Programming languages do not like this, and VBA is no exception, since there is no real-number solution when dividing by zero. When this happens, VBA will display a run-time error message and abruptly halt the subroutine (a dreaded *crash*), most likely leaving the user confused and frustrated. Run-time error messages are notoriously obscure, and generally provide no real useful information to the average user as to why the application crashed. A run-time error will usually be accompanied by an error *number*, but the number really doesn't mean much to the amateur programmer or user, especially if they do not know what triggered the error. Dividing by zero is one example where a run-time message is actually descriptive enough to tip off the user as to what the problem is. Clicking the Debug button on the message window (Figure 28) will show the programmer where the offense took place.

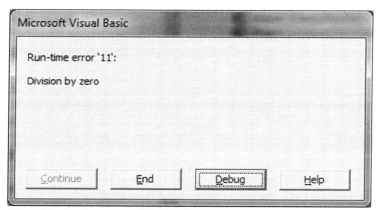

Figure 28. Run-time error, "Division by zero".

Though HEC-RAS is a very robust, user-friendly software application, like most software, it is no stranger to the occasional run-time error. Anyone who has used HEC-RAS for any length of time has no doubt triggered a run-time error, causing the software to abruptly halt and close. At best this can be a nuisance, requiring the user to track down the error in input data so that it can be fixed. Many times the error simply cannot be troubleshot, and the user is left with one option: notifying HEC so that it can be fixed for the next version of HEC-RAS. HEC's goal, as should be the goal for any software developer, is for no run time errors to ever show up. The code should be sophisticated enough to "catch" potential errors, before VBA does, and provide a coding strategy to avoid a crash. This is called "Error Handling". It is a strategy that should be employed in any computer program, especially those that will be run by users other than the programmer. The concept involves predicting a potential input error (or any other error for that matter), and writing in code to programmatically handle that error and prevent a crash. Typically this involves either forcing a corrective action in the code or prompting the user to enter a proper input value-one that won't make the program crash (i.e. displaying a message box that requests the user to enter a non-zero number, in the event that that number will be placed in the denominator of an equation). This is easier said than done; it's nearly impossible to catch all potential errors in an application, which is why bug-fixing is typically an interactive and on-going exercise between user and programmer. That being said, error handling is a programming strategy that should be employed, and ultimately leads to a more robust and user-friendly application.

VBA provides the programmer error handling ability that is somewhat archaic, when compared to more sophisticated programming languages, including VB. The programmer must first anticipate a potential bug and then add language that will bypass that bug and run other code to either correct the bug or inform the user of the problem. The goal is to prevent a run-time error message and ultimate crash of the software.

In VBA there are a number of statements that can be used for error handling. Some of the more common ones are:

- On Error

- Resume Next

- Goto

- Exit

The **On Error** statement tells VBA that if an error does occur, do whatever comes after the **On Error** statement. So an **On Error** statement has to be followed by some instructions. **Resume Next** is a convenient statement that merely tells VBA to ignore the error and move on to the next line of code. No error handling is actually done, VBA will just ignore and resume. Resume Next should be used only if you know that the error is not fatal (i.e. won't lead to a crash), and won't negatively affect the progress of the procedure being run or its results. The following code demonstrates the use of the **Resume Next** error handling strategy.

```
Sub ErrorHandlingExample1()

    '*************************************************************
    'Demonstrates Error Handling using Resume Next.

    'Written by Christopher Goodell
    'December 11, 2013

    'Uses an input box to request a number from the user to _
        divide 100 by.  A message box will return the answer. _
        If the user enters 0 or a non-number the code will _
        ignore the error and return VBA's nomenclature for an _
        infinite number:  1#INF.
    '*************************************************************

    Dim sngInput As Single
    Dim sngResult As Single

    On Error Resume Next
    sngInput = InputBox("Enter a number to divide 100 by.")
    sngResult = 100 / sngInput
    MsgBox "The answer is " & sngResult & "."

End Sub
```

The Input Box function displays an input box for the user to enter a number. However, in order to catch a potential error (for example, the user enters a value of 0, or a non-number), the **On Error** statement must be placed prior to the line of code that could throw a run-time error, in this case trying to divide 100 by 0. Here, **On Error Resume Next** is used to ignore the error and continue on with the next line of code. Without the **On Error Resume Next** line, VBA would have thrown a run time error message (like Figure 28) and halted the program. With the **On Error Resume Next** line, VBA continues on with the code and displays a message box giving the result. If 0 is input by the user, the message box will look like:

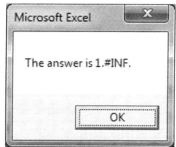

Figure 29. Result of dividing by zero.

The program did not crash, but instead displayed the message box with the result, "**1.#INF.**" "**1.#INF.** is VBA's nomenclature for an infinite number. A wise programmer would add more code to force the user to enter a non-zero number, but this demonstrates the **Resume Next** statement for error handling.

The **Goto** statement instructs VBA, upon encountering an error, to go to some other segment of code, which starts with an established Label. Therefore, every **Goto** statement must be followed by a Label ending in a colon (:). This allows the programmer to handle the error by issuing some additional code to take care of the problem. The following code uses the **Goto** command with a label, **ErrHandle:**. Upon encountering an error, VBA will then skip down to **ErrHandle:** in the code and proceed through the succeeding lines. It's important to put the **Exit Sub** (or **Exit Function**) statement just prior to the error handling code, so that if the program runs smoothly without errors, VBA doesn't proceed through the error handling code at the end of the procedure. **Exit Sub** bypasses error handling and exits the subroutine. In this example, the program will display a message box that requests the user enter a non-zero real number. Notice that the message was left purposefully vague. It didn't outright state that the user entered a value of 0. That is so other possible invalid entries will also be covered under the error handling. For example, if the user entered text instead of a number. It's a good idea to be as specific as possible in error handling messages, but not so specific to preclude other potential errors, which could lead to a confused and frustrated user.

```
Sub ErrorHandlingExample2()

    '****************************************************
    'Demonstrates Error Handling using the Goto statement.

    'Written by Christopher Goodell
    'December 11, 2013

    'Uses an input box to request a number from the user to _
        divide 100 by.  A message box will return the answer. _
        If the user enters 0 or a non-number the code will _
        go to error handling and return a message telling the _
        user to try again with a non-zero real number.
    '****************************************************

    Dim sngInput As Single
    Dim sngResult As Single

    On Error GoTo ErrHandle:
    sngInput = InputBox("Enter a number to divide 100 by.")
    sngResult = 100 / sngInput
    MsgBox "The answer is " & sngResult & "."

    Exit Sub
ErrHandle:
    MsgBox "Please try again with a non-zero real number."

End Sub
```

The **Goto** statement used to be commonplace in programming architecture, but contemporary professional computer programmers are offended by its use and consider **Goto** to be outdated-even prehistoric. Just Google™ the phrase "Goto Programming" and see how many negative articles show up. *"Using Goto is bad programming"*, *"Goto still considered harmful?"*, *"Is it ever worthwhile using Goto?"* just to name a few results. Quite simply, it's generally frowned upon by the professional computer programming community, which is understandable. Liberal use of the **Goto** statement creates a very disjointed, unsophisticated code structure. Though it was commonplace decades ago, it is rarely used in most codes today. However, to handle errors in VBA, **Goto** is still relevant (for now), so use it as necessary.

With a simple error like the user entering a zero or non-number, error handling could be achieved explicitly without resorting to an **On Error** command. A more elegant approach would force the user to correct the error immediately and then resume the code. This can be accomplished by inserting the **InputBox** function within a conditional **Do Loop**, checking the validity of the value entered by the user. The following code will force the user to enter a valid number by looping over the **InputBox** function until the entered value agrees with the conditional-in this case a non-zero numerical value. Notice that **sngInput** is set as a Variant data type in this example. This is to prevent a run time error thrown if the user enters a non-numerical value.

```vba
Sub ErrorHandlingExample3()

    '***********************************************************
    'Demonstrates explicit Error Handling using a Do Loop.

    'Written by Christopher Goodell
    'December 11, 2013

    'Uses an input box to request a number from the user to _
        divide 100 by.  A message box will return the answer. _
        If the user enters 0 or a non-number the code will _
        loop with another input box until the user enters a _
        non-zero real number.
    '***********************************************************
    Dim sngInput As Variant
    Dim sngResult As Single

    'Check for zero or non-numeric values
    Do
        sngInput = InputBox("Enter a number to divide 100 by.")
    Loop Until IsNumeric(sngInput) And sngInput <> 0

    sngResult = 100 / sngInput
    MsgBox "The answer is " & sngResult & "."

End Sub
```

6

EXAMPLE APPLICATIONS

Writing Output by River Station

Perhaps one of the most common uses of the HECRASController is to automate the retrieval of output for an array of cross sections. In order to effectively do this for multiple cross sections, it's important to think of the geometric components in a hierarchical sense. At the top of the hierarchy is the geometry file itself. Next would be rivers, then reaches, then nodes (cross sections, bridges, culverts, inline structures, etc.). If we were to organize an HEC-RAS project into a project tree, it might look something like Figure 30. Each HEC-RAS project can have multiple geometry files. Each geometry file can have multiple rivers. Each river can have multiple reaches, and each reach can have multiple nodes (river stations). And within each of the geometry components, there can be a number of different attributes. For example, a river might have information about the x-y coordinates that make up its stream centerline. A node would have information about station elevation points, or Manning's n values. As you can see, a geometry file is really made up of arrays within arrays within arrays, etc. Knowing this, provides a roadmap for programming the automation process of retrieving and storing output for cross sections.

Figure 30. HEC-RAS Project Tree.

The following code demonstrates the use of the data type in VBA (similar to the structure command in VB). A data type and its attributes are defined outside the scope of any function or subroutine. A data type can also have, as one of its attributes, a variable defined as another data type. For example, a "Reach" data type can have a variable defined as a "node" data type. The following code illustrates how data types are a convenient way to retrieve and store information using the HECRASController.

The first block of code shows the data type definition code that is used in this example. This block of code should go at the very top of your VBA module, before any subroutines or functions you may have written (or will be writing).

Once added to the module, you'll see these data types available in the auto-complete drop down box when you declare new variables. Notice how the **TypeRASGeom** data type, which is at the top of our HEC-RAS hierarchy, is listed last. That's so it can reference other lower level data types that have already been declared in the code. Since the **TypeRASGeom** data type in the code below has an attribute called **Riv()** defined as **TypeRiv**, then the **TypeRiv** data type must be coded before (above) the **TypeRASGeom** data type. The example below contains only what is necessary to get stage and flow for every node in an HEC-RAS project. Each of these data types can have many more attributes; input data or output data.

```vba
Type TypeNode 'Node Type
    RiverStation As String
    NodeID As Long
    NodeType As String
    nProf As Long
    ProfName() As String
    Stage() As Single
    Flow() As Single
    StageInitial As Double
    StageAtTarget As Double
    TimeInitial As String
    TimeAtTarget As String
End Type

Type TypeRch 'Reach Type
    nNode As Long
    Node() As TypeNode
    RchName As String
    RchID As Long
End Type

Type TypeRiv 'River Type
    nRch As Long
    Rch() As TypeRch
    RivName As String
    RivID As Long
End Type

Type TypeRASGeom 'Ras Geometry Type
    nRiv As Long
    Riv() As TypeRiv
End Type
```

The next block of code is a function called **GetRiversReachesNodes** that returns the geometric component arrays. This function retrieves all of the rivers, reaches, and nodes using the **Geometry_GetRivers**, **Geometry_GetReaches**, and

Geometry_GetNodes subroutines.   It also uses the **Output_GetProfiles** subroutine to determine the number of profiles so that can be added as an attribute to the **TypeNode** data type. It uses embedded For-Next loops at multiple levels to quantify the number of each geometric component and to populate the HEC-RAS geometry hierarchy.

```
Public Function GetRiversReachesNodes(ByRef typRASGeometry _
    As TypeRASGeom, RC As RAS500.HECRASController) As Boolean

    '*********************************************************
    'Demonstrates the Geometry_GetRivers, Geometry_GetReaches, _
        and Geometry_GetNodes subroutines

    'Written by Christopher Goodell
    'August 14, 2012

    'This retrieves all of the rivers, reaches, and nodes _
        from the geometry file and organizes them into _
        "Types". Returns a geometry structure called _
        typRASGeometry.
    '*********************************************************

    With typRASGeometry
        Dim strRiv() As String, strRch() As String
        Dim strNode() As String, strNodeType() As String
        Dim lngRiv As Long, lngRch As Long, lngNode As Long

        'Determine number of profiles
        Dim lngProf As Long
        Dim strProf() As String
        RC.Output_GetProfiles lngProf, strProf()

        'Populate the RASGeometry Type
        'Call the Geometry_GetRivers subroutine to get the
        '    rivers.
        RC.Geometry_GetRivers lngRiv, strRiv()

        Dim i As Long, j As Long, k As Long
        For i = 1 To lngRiv
            ReDim Preserve .Riv(1 To i)
            .nRiv = i
            .Riv(i).RivID = i
            .Riv(i).RivName = strRiv(i)

            'Call the Geometry_GetReaches subroutine to get
            '    the reaches.
            With .Riv(i)
                RC.Geometry_GetReaches i, lngRch, strRch()
                For j = 1 To lngRch
                    ReDim Preserve .Rch(1 To j)
                    .nRch = j
                    .Rch(j).RchID = j
                    .Rch(j).RchName = strRch(j)

                    'Call the Geometry_GetNodes subroutine to
```

```
            '    get the nodes.
            With .Rch(j)
                RC.Geometry_GetNodes i, j, lngNode, _
                    strNode(), strNodeType()
                For k = 1 To lngNode
                    ReDim Preserve .Node(1 To k)
                    .nNode = k
                    .Node(k).NodeID = k
                    .Node(k).RiverStation = strNode(k)
                    .Node(k).NodeType = strNodeType(k)
                    .Node(k).nProf = lngProf
                Next k
            End With

        Next j
        End With

    Next i
    End With

    GetRiversReachesNodes = True

End Function
```

The final block of code for this example is a subroutine called **WriteRiversReachNodes**. This subroutine takes the Geometry components that were constructed in the **GetRiversReachesNode** function and adds stage and flow data to the array of nodes. To conclude, it prints out a message box that lists all of the nodes by river/reach, and their respective flows and stages. Again, using For-Next loops, the code drills down to the node level and then uses the **Output_NodeOutput** function to get the desired output variables. To use the **Output_NodeOutput** function, you have to provide arguments for the river ID, reach ID, node ID, the up/down reference (only used for bridges/culverts/multiple openings), the profile number, and the variable ID number. From the list of HEC-RAS variables in Appendix E, water surface elevation has an ID number of 2 and total flow has an ID number of 9. The string value (**strGeomList**) is constructed along the way, with each river, reach, node, and output values added as they are encountered in the For-Next loop.

```
Sub WriteRiversReachesNodes()

    '*************************************************************
    'Demonstrates Compute_CurrentPlan function

    'Written by Christopher Goodell
    'December 6, 2012

    'Writes a string that lists all rivers, reaches, nodes, _
        and their stage and flow values for the first _
        profile.  Calls the zGetRiversReachesNodes function.
```

```
'Tested with the BeavCrek.prj and 3ReachUnsteady.prj data _
    sets.  Any HEC-RAS project will work.
'*******************************************************

'Open an HEC-RAS Project
Dim RC As New RAS500.HECRASController
zOpenRASProjectByRef RC

'Run the Project so there's output to retrieve
Dim blnDidItWork As Boolean
Dim lngMsg As Long, strMsg() As String
blnDidItWork = RC.Compute_CurrentPlan(lngMsg, strMsg())

'Populate a RAS Geometry Type using the _
    GetRiverReachesNodes Function
Dim typRASGeometry As mRASController.TypeRASGeom
blnDidItWork = mRASController.zGetRiversReachesNodes _
    (typRASGeometry, RC)

'Write a string called strGeomList that contains all _
    Rivers, Reaches, NodesAgain,  and their stages and _
    flows. strGeomList gets text added to it for every _
    new geometric component.

Dim strGeomList As String
Dim i As Long, j As Long, k As Long

'Rivers
For i = 1 To typRASGeometry.nRiv

    'Reaches
    With typRASGeometry.Riv(i)
        For j = 1 To .nRch
            strGeomList = strGeomList & .RivName & ", " & _
                .Rch(j).RchName & Chr(13)
            strGeomList = strGeomList & "RS" & Chr(9) & _
                "Stage (ft)" & Chr(9) & "Flow (cfs)" & _
                Chr(13)

            'Nodes
            With .Rch(j)
                For k = 1 To .nNode
                    Application.StatusBar = "Working " & _
                        "on River " & i & ", Reach " & _
                        j & ", RS " & _
                        Trim(.Node(k).RiverStation) & "."

                    ReDim .Node(k).Stage(1 To 1)
                    .Node(k).Stage(1) = _
                        RC.Output_NodeOutput(i, j, k, 2, _
                        1, 2)

                    ReDim .Node(k).Flow(1 To 1)
                    .Node(k).Flow(1) = _
                        RC.Output_NodeOutput(i, j, k, 2, _
                        1, 9)
```

```
                strGeomList = strGeomList & _
                    .Node(k).RiverStation & _
                    .Node(k).NodeType & Chr(9) & _
                    Round(.Node(k).Stage(1), 2) & _
                    Chr(9) & .Node(k).Flow(1) & Chr(13)
                Next k
                strGeomList = strGeomList & Chr(13)
            End With

        Next j
    End With

    Next i

    'Show the string
    MsgBox strGeomList

    'Close HEC-RAS
    RC.QuitRAS

End Sub
```

Running HEC-RAS in a Monte Carlo Simulation

Monte Carlo is a commonly used method for approximating solution outcomes where inputs have a high degree of uncertainty. Introduced by Stanislaw Ulam and coined by John von Neumann in the 1940's for use in support of nuclear weapons research, Monte Carlo applications today vary broadly, supporting risk-based decision-making efforts in various fields of science, engineering, insurance, finance, and even sports. Until recently, making use of Monte Carlo methods for probabilistic analysis in flood studies has been difficult, namely due to the lack of computing power afforded to the typical "desktop" engineer. For statistically valid results, a Monte Carlo simulation can require repeated realizations numbering in the 10's or 100's of thousands, depending on the number of sampled input parameters and the acceptable error. Running one realization of even a modestly complex unsteady HEC-RAS model can take minutes or more, the total simulation time often depending on the skill of the modeler. A one-minute long model realization, run 10,000 times would take nearly seven days! For this technique to be practical to an HEC-RAS modeler, an automated process is required. The HECRASController and the ability to read and write to HEC-RAS input files makes this possible.

Let's say we've identified our selection of Manning's n values in our HEC-RAS model as a significant source of input uncertainty (it always is). Rather than selecting our "best approximation" of Manning's n values with the traditional deterministic approach, we've decided to acknowledge the uncertainty and quantify it in our results by using the Monte Carlo Method to generate probabilities of outcomes. This requires first defining the statistical distribution of possible Manning's n values at each cross section. You may be able to assign what you could call the *expected* Manning's n value, or mean value, by consulting a variety of photo references of similar rivers or streams, equations, experience and judgment, or a combination of all. However, a truthful modeler will acknowledge that this approximation could realistically be in error by a significant margin, perhaps as high as plus or minus 25 percent. To capture this uncertainty in the input Manning's n values, a normal distribution (the bell-shaped curve) can be constructed with the mean set to the expected Manning's n value, and the standard distribution defined so that the majority of possible inputs fall in the "meat" of the bell shaped curve. Figure 31 demonstrates a simple normal distribution of possible Manning's n values. The expected, or mean Manning's n value for this cross section is 0.04, represented by the symbol μ. Here, the modeler defines her confidence in her ability to predict Manning's n values by establishing a plus or minus range of 25 percent (0.03 on the low end and 0.05 on the high end). Setting these bounds to plus or minus two standard deviations (σ) indicates that she believes with 95.4 percent confidence that the true Manning's n value will be between 0.03 and 0.05, concentrated around the expected value of 0.03 by a normal distribution. For each realization in the Monte Carlo simulation, a Manning's n value will be randomly sampled, about the normal distribution. In theory, and with enough realizations, 95.4 percent of the randomly sampled Manning's n values will be between 0.03 and 0.05 and the mean of all sampled Manning's n values will be 0.04. In other words, the sampled Manning's n values will follow the shape of the established normal distribution.

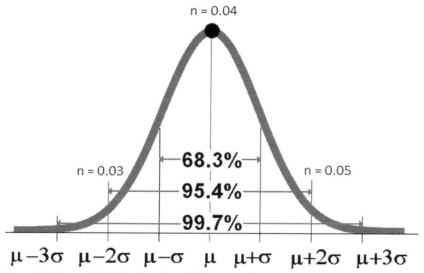

Figure 31. Normal Distribution of Possible Manning's n Values.

To achieve statistical convergence, and thereby an accurate representation of the probability of outcomes, a LOT of realizations (HEC-RAS runs) are necessary, typically numbering in the 10's or 100's of thousands. You could handle this by sitting at your desk, waiting for each HEC-RAS run to complete and pressing the compute button again, again, and again, while changing the Manning's n value each time. This, of course, is outrageous, and may very well get you fired from your job. Alternatively, you could design an application that does this automatically for you. I prefer the latter.

The programming approach is simple and follows these basic steps in the code:

1. Randomly sample inputs about the pre-defined statistical distribution of possible Manning's n values.

2. Open the HEC-RAS geometry text file for reading and writing. Replace the previous Manning's n values with the newly sampled ones.

3. Using the HECRASController, open and run the HEC-RAS model.

4. Using the HECRASController, retrieve the desired output and store it to an array.

5. Repeat.

Once the full number of realizations has been run, your application will sort the output data and a simple ranking provides the exceedance probabilities, based on the uncertainty of input Manning's n values. Instead of presenting a single water surface elevation at a given cross section (the deterministic approach), now you're able to provide a probabilistic distribution of possible water surface elevations, which inherently acknowledges the uncertainty of the Manning's n values and provides the "odds" of being flooded. Instead of producing a single, deterministically derived flood inundation map, you can produce an exceedance probability inundation (EPI) map, an example of which is presented in Figure 32. This figure demonstrates the advantage of a probabilistic approach, namely the communication of uncertainty in the results. The deterministically derived flood inundation falsely claims that a flood of a given frequency will produce a flood inundation represented by the red outline and properties B, C, and D will be flooded. That very well may be the case, should that flood event happen, but it is disingenuous to make that claim. By running a probabilistic approach using the Monte Carlo Method, we can rightly acknowledge that we don't know exactly what the flood inundation will look like, but we can state probabilities of inundation. Properties B, and C have a 10 percent chance of being flooded, while property D is 50 percent likely to be flooded for the investigated flood event. It is highly unlikely that Property A will be flooded at all. In addition to being a more genuine presentation of the results, a probabilistic analysis allows for follow-up risk-informed decision-making for planning studies and an evaluation of economic consequences.

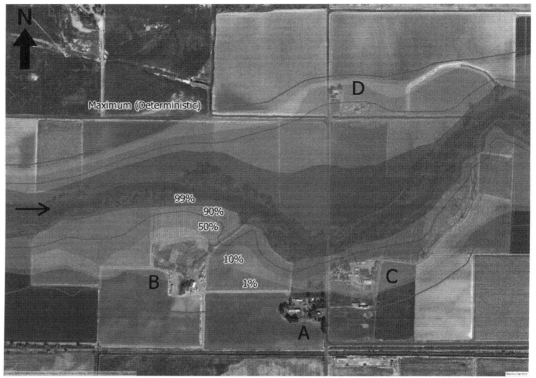

Figure 32. Exceedance Probability Inundation Map (Goodell, Christopher R., "Moving Towards Risk-Based Dam Breach Modeling", Proceedings, Dam Safety 2013 Conference, Providence, Rhode Island, September, 2013).

The following code demonstrates a simplified approach to applying Monte Carlo to an HEC-RAS model. While this subroutine only addresses the uncertainty of Manning's n values for the sake of demonstration, a probabilistic approach should evaluate all significant uncertain input values that go into an HEC-RAS model. These might include discharge coefficients, boundary conditions, and even computational parameters such as computation interval, implicit weighting factor, and computation tolerances. For dam breach models, the uncertainty of the breach parameters (ultimate size, shape, and formation time of the breach) would be incorporated into a probabilistic approach. In fact, breach parameters have been found to have an order of magnitude more sensitivity than n values for typical dam breach studies.

The subroutine **MonteCarloNValues**() begins by defining the normal distribution of Manning's n values. The variable **sngMeanN**, a single precision floating point number, is set to the expected Manning's n value of 0.04. A standard deviation of 0.005 is defined next. This establishes a 95.4 percent confidence that the Manning's n values will fall between 0.03 and 0.05.

The next block of code opens HEC-RAS using the **Project_Open** function, with **strRASProj** being the path and project file we want to open. "Critical Creek" is one of the standard steady flow datasets that come with the HEC-RAS software.

In this subroutine, a new geometry text file will be created for each realization, with the main channel Manning's n values resampled each time. To do this, the code builds the new text file by copying the original geometry text file, line by line, only changing the line of text that includes the main channel Manning's n value. The string variable **strRASGeom** is the original geometry text file, including path, and **strTmpRASGeom** will be the newly constructed text files with the sampled Manning's n values.

The next section of code begins the **For-Next** loop, each loop representing one realization in the Monte Carlo simulation. The integer **intNumRealizations** is set equal to 100 in this example, however the total number of realizations should be large enough to ensure statistical converge of the computed mean and standard deviation of the sampled Manning's n values. A test for convergence could be included in the **For-Next** loop by recomputing the mean and standard deviation of the sampled Manning's n Values from the previous realizations. Once the computed mean and standard deviation are equal (within some tolerance) to the predefined mean (0.04) and standard deviation (0.005), an **Exit For** command could be inserted to abort the **For-Next** loop and continue on with the code.

The first step for each realization is to randomly sample a Manning's n value about the predefined normal distribution. The **Rnd** function (VBA library, Math Class) returns a random number between 0 and 1. However, VBA, by default, will cycle through the same random numbers, so that after enough samples, a repeated pattern will develop. To avoid this, the **Randomize** subroutine is called, which initializes the random number generator and eliminates the recycling of random numbers. With a random number of domain [0,1] generated, we can transform it around the normal distribution we pre-defined, by first subtracting 0.5 (domain [-0.5, +0.5]) and then multiplying by the standard deviation and adding the mean. Therefore, a random number of 0.5, will be transformed to the mean Manning's n value of 0.04, as we'd expect.

Now that we have the randomly generated Manning's n value, **sngRandNValue**, we can insert that into the geometry text file. This is accomplished by opening the original geometry text file, reading it line by line, while at the same time creating a new geometry file. The new file will be an exact copy of the original, only the main channel Manning's n value for each cross section will be set to the sampled value. To access the geometry text files, the **Open** subroutine is used. The file we're reading (the original geometry file) will be open as Input, since we're only reading it. The new geometry text file will be opened **For Output**, so that we can write to it. Each iteration of the **Do-Loop** represents a line in the text file. The added **While Not EOF(1)** tells VBA that once the End of the File (**EOF**) is reached, then quit looping and move on with the rest of the code.

Inside the **Do-Loop**, the **Line Input** command instructs VBA to read the next line in the text file and set **strTextline** to that string. If nowhere in that line is the partial string "#Mann=" then VBA is instructed to print **strTextline** to the write file, **strTmpRASGeom** and then loop to the next line. If "#Mann=" is included anywhere in the line, then we've found the Manning's n value key. However, the Manning's n values are actually listed out in Fields of 8 starting on the line after the #Mann=" line. So another Line Input is needed to access and edit the line of text with the main channel Manning's n value.

The next line in the geometry text file looks something like this:

0 .1 0 720 0.04 0 765 .1 0

This is an example of data structured into delimited Fields of 8. The first value, "0", is the starting stationing for the left overbank Manning's n value and the second value is the left overbank Manning's n value. The third value is always set to 0. The next three values represent the main channel, and the final three represent the right overbank. The 0.04 is the value that we want to change. To do this, we have to first parse out the nine values that are set as a single string value (**strTextLine**) in the line to nine separate string values. That will allow us to remove to 0.04 and replace it with the newly sampled Manning's n value. The **ParseStringbyEights** is a subroutine I wrote to handle parsing data delimited in Fields of 8. **ParseStringbyEights** code is included in this chapter directly after the **MonteCarloNValues** subroutine. Once the main channel Manning's n value is replaced, the line of text is rebuilt using the **PutInFields** function (code also included after the **MonteCarloNValues** subroutine) and written to the new geometry text file using the **Print** command. Once all lines in the original text file are read and copied into the new text file, we've reached the end of the file (**EOF**) and the **Do-Loop** is completed.

Once access to the geometry text files is no longer needed, they need to be closed. While they are open for input or output, they are more-or-less untouchable. They can't be copied or deleted until they are closed. In fact, if left open, the next command, **FileCopy**, will throw a Run Time error.

FileCopy is used to overwrite the original geometry text file with the new one. Now that **strTmpRASGeom** is no longer needed, it's a good idea to delete it-this is accomplished using the **Kill** subroutine. To finish the realization, the HECRASController subroutine, **Project_Open**, is used to reopen the HEC-RAS project. This is a necessary step, even though the project is already open, since reopening it reads the new geometry data into memory. Without reopening the project, the same original geometry would be used for each realization and the same water surface elevation would be computed each time. Next HEC-RAS is computed using the HECRASController function, **Compute_CurrentPlan**. While **MonteCarloNValues** is running, you'll notice the HEC-RAS computation window open, run, and close, in very quick succession, for each realization. On my computer, each realization takes about ½ second, so the opening, running, and closing of HEC-RAS looks somewhat like a strobe light-a bit annoying. Furthermore, repeated opening and closing of windows consumes computational resources, ultimately making the subroutine run slower. A quicker overall simulation could be run by calling the HECRASController subroutine, **Compute_HideComputationWindow** just prior to calling **Compute_CurrentPlan**. Be careful though, because hiding the computation window takes away the only explicit evidence you have that the Monte Carlo simulation is progressing smoothly. Without visual cues to verify the subroutine is working as it should, you might wonder if the code is stuck in an infinite loop, or otherwise locked up. Adding in some visual cues like changing the cursor to an hourglass, giving status updates in the Excel® status bar, including a progress bar, or list of messages (as demonstrated in Chapter 5) can help inform the user of the progress of the simulation when the HEC-RAS computation window is kept hidden.

The final step for a given realization is to retrieve the water surface elevation output for our selected cross section (based on the newly sampled Manning's n value). Output can be retrieved using the HECRASController function **Output_NodeOutput**. **Output_NodeOutput** requires six arguments to be passed. They are, in order:

1. River ID

2. Reach ID

3. Node ID

4. Up/Down index for nodes with multiple sections (only used for bridges)

5. Profile Number

6. Output ID. The ID for Water Surface Elevation is 2 (see Appendix E)

The water surface elevation is then stored in the array, **sngWSElev**. **ReDim** is used to redimension the array to the number of water surface elevations that are stored in it. The **ReDim** command by itself would set the number of indices for the array, but would also initialize the array, wiping out any data that's already in it (from the previous realizations). Adding the **Preserve** command does just that-it allows the dimensioning, but preserves all data already in the array.

Once all realizations have been run (in the **For-Next** loop), the water surface elevations in **sngWSElev** array have to be resorted, low to high, to establish exceedance probabilities. The next block of code does this through a **Do-Loop**. The values in **sngWSElev** are compared to each other, one-by one. If a water surface elevation for one index is found to be greater than a water surface elevation at the next higher index, then those two values swap indices. By running this check through all indices, the array will sort itself low to high.

With a sorted array of water surface elevations, at node "7", water surface elevations can be assigned to various exceedance probabilities by determining percentiles. For example, the 99 percent exceedance probability water surface elevation is the water surface elevation that resides at index (1/100)***intNumRealizations**. If we have 1000 realizations that are sorted from low to high then the 99 percent exceedance probability water surface elevation will be the water surface elevation that occupies index number 10. There are more sophisticated methods for determining exceedance probabilities, and they probably should be used for smaller numbers of realizations. However, this brute-force method works fine for most Monte Carlo applications, where the number of realizations is high (1000's +).

With the exceedance probability water surface elevations established, the last step is to pass that information on to the user. This can be done any number of ways, including populating a table in Excel®, writing to a text file, or simply including it in a message box window. Here the exceedance probability water surface elevations are built into a single string variable, **strOutput**. Once **strOutput** is constructed, it is passed to the **MsgBox** subroutine and the following window should open on your desktop:

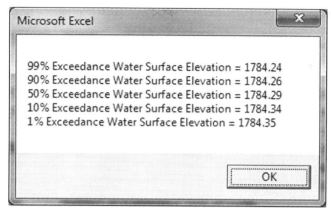

Figure 33. Exceedance Probability Water Surface Elevations.

If you use the same number of realizations (100) when you run this subroutine, you'll find that each time you run it, you'll get slightly different results for the different exceedance water surface elevations. Increasing the number of realizations until you have statistical convergence will take care of this problem. The results indicate that water surface elevation at Node 7 is not very sensitive to Manning's n value. In fact, the Monte Carlo simulation suggests that there's a 98 percent probability that the water surface elevation will be between 1784.24 ft and 1784.35 ft.

This code was written in part to demonstrate strategies for reading and writing from/to HEC-RAS text files. The Manning's n values could alternately be edited for each realization using the HECRASController **Geometry_SetMannLChR** function.

```
Sub MonteCarloNValues()

    '*********************************************************
    'Demonstrates running HEC-RAS in a Monte Carlo Experiment.

    'Written by Christopher Goodell
    'November 7, 2013

    'This subroutine randomly samples n values about a normal _
        distribution and applies that n value to the main _
        channel of each cross section.  The HEC-RAS project _
        is re-run after each sampling.  Water surface _
        elevations are stored at the completion of each _
        realization and finally sorted to determine elevation _
        exceedance probabilities.

    'Tested with the CRITCREK.prj data set.  Code would have _
        to be slightly modified to work with other data sets.
    '*********************************************************

    'Keep track of time
    Dim timStartTime As Variant, timNowTime As Variant, _
        timElapseTime As Variant
    timStartTime = Timer
```

```
'Define the normal distribution of n values to use.
Dim sngMeanN As Single
Dim sngStdDevN As Single
sngMeanN = 0.04 'mean, or expected value.
sngStdDevN = 0.015 'This sets 2 standard deviations to _
                            plus and minus 0.03 (50%), or _
                            Manning's n values of 0.01 to 0.07.


'Open the HEC-RAS project
Dim RC As New RAS500.HECRASController
Dim strRASProj As String 'HEC-RAS Project

Dim sngWSElev() As Single
    'The array of computed water surface elevations for _
        each realization.

strRASProj = "C:\AutomateHECRAS\Steady Examples\" & _
    "CRITCREK.prj"

'Open the HEC-RAS project Critical Creek - Example 1
RC.Project_Open (strRASProj)

'Get all of the geometry into a Geometry Type
Dim typGeom As mSamples.TypeRASGeom
Dim blnGotIt As Boolean
blnGotIt = GetRiversReachesNodes(typGeom, RC)

'Define variables used in the For-Next Loop
Dim intNumMessages As Long
Dim strMessages() As String
Dim blnDidItCompute As Boolean
Dim strRiv As String, strRch As String, strRS As String
Dim sngNL As Single, sngNCh As Single, sngNR As Single
Dim strErrMsg As String
Dim sngSumMean As Single, sngCompMean As Single
Dim sngAllRandN() As Single

'Loop through each realization
Dim intNumRealizations As Integer
intNumRealizations = 1000 'This number should be large _
    enough to reach statistical convergence on the _
    computed mean and standard deviation of sampled n _
    Values.
ReDim sngAllRandN(1 To intNumRealizations)
Dim i As Integer, j As Integer, k As Integer, l As Integer
For i = 1 To intNumRealizations
    'Get n value to use by randomly sampling about the _
        normal distribution
    sngNL = 0.1
    sngNCh = CSng(GetRandomNormal(sngMeanN, sngStdDevN))
    sngNR = 0.1

    'Keep running tab of the computed mean
    sngAllRandN(i) = sngNCh
    sngSumMean = sngSumMean + sngNCh
```

```
        sngCompMean = Round((sngSumMean / i), 4)

        'Apply new n values to geometry
        For j = 1 To typGeom.nRiv
            With typGeom.Riv(j)
                strRiv = .RivName
                For k = 1 To .nRch
                    With .Rch(k)
                        strRch = .RchName
                        For l = 1 To .nNode
                            strRS = .Node(l).RiverStation
                            RC.Geometry_SetMann_LChR strRiv, _
                                strRch, strRS, sngNL, sngNCh, _
                                sngNR, strErrMsg
                        Next l
                    End With
                Next k
            End With
        Next j

        'Save the project with new Manning's n values
        RC.Project_Save

        'Compute the HEC-RAS project
        RC.Compute_HideComputationWindow
        blnDidItCompute = RC.Compute_CurrentPlan _
            (intNumMessages, strMessages())

        'Get water surface elevation output at River 1, Reach _
            1, River Station 7, for profile 1.  The Output ID _
            for water surface elevation is 2.
        ReDim Preserve sngWSElev(i)
        sngWSElev(i) = RC.Output_NodeOutput(1, 1, 7, 0, 1, 2)

        'Show Progress
        timNowTime = Timer
        timElapseTime = _
            Round((timNowTime - timStartTime) / 60, 2)
        Application.StatusBar = "Finished computing " & _
            "realization #" & i & " of " & intNumRealizations _
            & ".  Sampled N Value = " & Round(sngNCh, 4) & _
            ". All Samples Mean N value = " & sngCompMean & _
            ". Elapsed Time: " & timElapseTime & "minutes."
    Next i

    'Close HEC-RAS
    RC.QuitRAS

    'Sort the water surface elevations low to high
    Dim blnSorted As Boolean
    Dim sngTemp As Single
    Dim intX As Integer
    blnSorted = False
    Do While Not blnSorted
        blnSorted = True
        For intX = 0 To UBound(sngWSElev) - 1
```

```
                If sngWSElev(intX) > sngWSElev(intX + 1) Then
                    sngTemp = sngWSElev(intX + 1)
                    sngWSElev(intX + 1) = sngWSElev(intX)
                    sngWSElev(intX) = sngTemp
                    blnSorted = False
                End If
        Next intX
    Loop

    'Determine the exceedance probability water surface _
        elevations.
    Dim sngWSEl99 As Single, sngWSEL90 As Single, _
        sngWSEL50 As Single, sngWSEL10 As Single, _
        sngWSEL1 As Single

    sngWSEl99 = sngWSElev(CInt(0.01 * UBound(sngWSElev)))
    sngWSEL90 = sngWSElev(CInt(0.1 * UBound(sngWSElev)))
    sngWSEL50 = sngWSElev(CInt(0.5 * UBound(sngWSElev)))
    sngWSEL10 = sngWSElev(CInt(0.9 * UBound(sngWSElev)))
    sngWSEL1 = sngWSElev(CInt(0.99 * UBound(sngWSElev)))

    'Send the exceedance probability water surface elevations _
        and computed mean to a message box.
    Dim strOutput As String
    strOutput = "99% Exceedance Water Surface Elevation = " & _
        Round(sngWSEl99, 2) & Chr(13)
    strOutput = strOutput & "90% Exceedance Water Surface " & _
        "Elevation = " & Round(sngWSEL90, 2) & Chr(13)
    strOutput = strOutput & "50% Exceedance Water Surface " & _
        "Elevation = " & Round(sngWSEL50, 2) & Chr(13)
    strOutput = strOutput & "10% Exceedance Water Surface " & _
        "Elevation = " & Round(sngWSEL10, 2) & Chr(13)
    strOutput = strOutput & "1% Exceedance Water Surface " & _
        "Elevation = " & Round(sngWSEL1, 2) & Chr(13)
    timElapseTime = Round((timNowTime - timStartTime) / 60, 1)
    MsgBox "Total time: " & timElapseTime & " minutes." & _
        Chr(13) & strOutput & "Computed Mean = " & _
        CStr(sngCompMean)

End Sub
```

Adding Stationing to Each Cross Section's Station-Elevation Table.

Occasionally I've been asked if there is a way to globally change the stationing for each cross section's station elevation table by a certain amount. Perhaps some of the cross sections have negative stationing values and the user wishes every cross section's station elevation table to start at 0. Maybe the user wants to center the invert of the channel at Station 0. Or the user may simply want to adjust the stationing of each cross section by some constant value.

In HEC-RAS, there is a useful tool to adjust stationing in the Station Elevation table-it's found under the Options menu item of the Cross Section Data Editor (Figure 34).

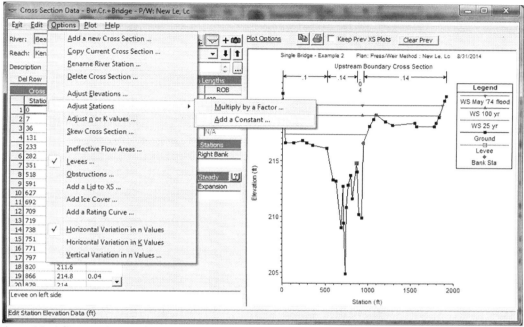

Figure 34. Adjust Stations in the Cross Section Data Editor.

Unfortunately, this tool can only be applied one cross section at a time. So this task must be performed once for each cross section, to globally change the stationing. It takes about 6 seconds to make this change for one cross section. If the HEC-RAS project has 1000 cross sections, this task would take an hour and forty minutes. If some automation code can be written in 30 minutes, then it would be worthwhile to write the code, taking advantage of your newfound knowledge of reading and writing to HEC-RAS text files. Much of automating HEC-RAS really boils down to levels of effort. *"Will it take more time and effort to write the code, or to just perform that task manually?"* Of course, there is some value to having another program added to your library of HEC-RAS automation utilities for future use, so perhaps you'll be willing to spend a little more time writing code than it would take to manually accomplish the task. But the bottom line is long tedious tasks should be weighed against the effort that would be required to write some automation code. It may be hard to approximate this at first, but once you have some experience writing HEC-RAS automation code, you'll be able to accurately make this call.

The following subroutine, **AddStationing**, adds a value of "100" to the stationing for each station elevation point for each cross section in the BEAVCREK.prj dataset. You'll notice that this code does not use the HECRASController, it strictly reads from and writes to the geometry text file. Once you get comfortable reading and writing HEC-RAS input text files, you may find the HECRASController unnecessary for many of the automation tasks you wish to perform, particularly if they are solely manipulation of input data. The subroutine **AddStationing** calls two external functions **ParseStringbyEights** and **PutInFields**. Both presented after the **AddStationing** subroutine.

After declaring some string variables, the subroutine begins by defining the read and write geometry text files, which in this example will be from the first geometry file (BEAVCREK.g01) of the BEAVCREK.prj dataset. The read file, **strReadFileName** is opened **For Input as #1**. The write file, **strWriteFileName** is opened **For Output as #2**.

Since the station elevation data for each cross section will be adjusted, a **Do-Loop** block is created to cycle through all of the cross sections, searching out the key that indicates a start of a block of station elevation data: #Sta/Elev. Once this key is found, the code will loop through all the lines of station elevation data until #Mann is found in the line. #Mann is the key for Manning's n values and is found immediately after the station elevation data.

Within the **Do-Loop**, the code parses out each line of station elevation data by using the **ParseStringbyEights** function. This function will return an array of "Parts", each part representing a string value from an 8-character long field (Field of 8). The geometry file includes five pairs of station elevation data per line, so there will be a maximum of 10 parts sent back from **ParseStringbyEights**. Next, the code adds "100" to every other Part, including Part 0, using a **For-Next** loop with a Step 2 qualifier. Parts 0, 2, 4, 6, and 8 are stations and Parts 1, 3, 5, 7, and 9 are elevations. If the last line in a block of station elevation data does not included a full five pairs, then the code will set the "unused" Parts equal to "", also known as a null string.

With the stationing Parts redefined, the new line of text can be constructed, using the **PutInFields** function. **PutInFields** takes 10 numbers and properly formats them into Fields of 8. The newly constructed line of text, **strNewStaElLine**, is added into the write file, **strWriteFileNamem**, using the **Print** subroutine.

Once the new geometry file is created, both the old and new are closed using the **Close** subroutine, and then the new text file set as the official BEAVCREK.g01 file. A final message box lets the user know that all stations have been increased by 100.

```
Sub AddStationing()

    '****************************************************************
    'Demonstrates how to make changes to all cross sections _
```

by reading and writing to an HEC-RAS text file.

```
'Written by Christopher Goodell
'Nov 11, 2013

'This subroutine goes through all of the cross sections _
    in a geometry file and adds 100 to the stationing _
    in the station elevation table.

'Tested with the BEAVCREK.g01 geometry file.
'*****************************************************

'Define the read and write geometry files.
Dim strReadFileName As String
Dim strWriteFileName As String
strReadFileName = "C:\AutomateHECRAS\Steady Examples\" & _
    "BEAVCREK.g01"
strWriteFileName = "C:\AutomateHECRAS\Steady Examples\" & _
    "BEAVCREK.g01temp"

'Open the read file for input, write file for output
Open strReadFileName For Input As #1
Open strWriteFileName For Output As #2

'Search for the start of station-elevation data
Dim i As Integer
Dim strTextLine As String, strNewStaElLine As String
Dim intLineNum As Integer
Do While Not EOF(1)
    Line Input #1, strTextLine
    intLineNum = intLineNum + 1
    If InStr(1, strTextLine, "#Sta/Elev") Then
        'This indicates the start of station-elevation data

        'Print this line and advance to the next line to _
            start reading in station-elevation data.
        Print #2, strTextLine
        Line Input #1, strTextLine
        intLineNum = intLineNum + 1

        Dim lngNumParts As Long
        Dim strPart() As String

        'When #Mann is found in the strTextLine, that _
            indicates the table of station elevation data _
            is complete.
        Do While InStr(1, strTextLine, "#Mann") = 0

            'This parses out the string into parts.  The _
                even numbered parts (including 0) are _
                stations, the odd numbered parts are _
                elevations.
            lngNumParts = mTxtReadWrite. _
                ParseStringbyEights(strTextLine, strPart())

            'This handles when a line does not have a _
```

```
                            full 5 station elevation pairs.
                    If lngNumParts < 10 Then
                        lngNumParts = 10
                        ReDim Preserve strPart(9)
                    End If

                    'Add 100 to each stationing and round to 1 _
                        decimal point.
                    For i = 0 To lngNumParts - 1 Step 2
                        If Not Trim(strPart(i)) = "" Then
                            strPart(i) = Round((CSng(strPart(i)) _
                                + 100), 1)
                        End If
                    Next i

                    'Rebuild the new line of station elevation _
                        pairs
                    strNewStaElLine = mTxtReadWrite.PutInFields _
                        (strPart(0), strPart(1), strPart(2), _
                        strPart(3), strPart(4), strPart(5), _
                        strPart(6), strPart(7), strPart(8), _
                        strPart(9))

                    'Print the new line of station elevation _
                        pairs to the temporary geometry file.
                    Print #2, strNewStaElLine

                    'Advance to the next line and repeat.
                    Line Input #1, strTextLine
                    intLineNum = intLineNum + 1
                Loop
                Print #2, strTextLine
            Else
                Print #2, strTextLine
            End If
        Loop

        'Close the text files
        Close #1
        Close #2

        'Replace the original geometry file with the temporary _
            one, then delete the temporary one.
        FileCopy strWriteFileName, strReadFileName
        Kill strWriteFileName

        'A message box to let the user know it's done.
        MsgBox "Done!  All Stations increased by 100."

End Sub


Function ParseStringbyEights(ByVal DataLine As String, _
    ByRef Part() As String) As Long

    '************************************************************
```

```
'This function parses an eight character string _
    delimited string variable into multiple strings.

'Written by Chris Goodell
'Oct 13, 2013
'*************************************************************

Dim pos() As Long
Dim i, nParts As Long
nParts = Len(DataLine) / 8

ReDim pos(nParts), Part(nParts)
For i = 0 To nParts - 1
    pos(i) = (8 * i) + 1
Next
'
'   Get data for every eight spaces
For i = 0 To nParts - 1
    Part(i) = Mid(DataLine, pos(i), 8)
Next i

'   Return the number of things found
ParseStringbyEights = nParts

End Function


Function PutInFields(ByVal Field1 As String, _
    ByVal Field2 As String, ByVal Field3 As String, _
    ByVal Field4 As String, ByVal Field5 As String, _
    ByVal Field6 As String, ByVal Field7 As String, _
    ByVal Field8 As String, ByVal Field9 As String, _
    ByVal Field10 As String) As String

    '*************************************************************
    'Puts the passed variables into a line of Fields of 8 _
        characters wide

    'Written by Christopher Goodell
    '*************************************************************

    Dim Fld() As String
    Dim i As Integer

    ReDim Fld(10)
    Fld(1) = Field1
    Fld(2) = Field2
    Fld(3) = Field3
    Fld(4) = Field4
    Fld(5) = Field5
    Fld(6) = Field6
    Fld(7) = Field7
    Fld(8) = Field8
    Fld(9) = Field9
    Fld(10) = Field10
```

```
For i = 1 To 10
    If Len(Fld(i)) = 0 Then Fld(i) = "        "
    If Len(Fld(i)) = 1 Then Fld(i) = "       " & Fld(i)
    If Len(Fld(i)) = 2 Then Fld(i) = "      " & Fld(i)
    If Len(Fld(i)) = 3 Then Fld(i) = "     " & Fld(i)
    If Len(Fld(i)) = 4 Then Fld(i) = "    " & Fld(i)
    If Len(Fld(i)) = 5 Then Fld(i) = "   " & Fld(i)
    If Len(Fld(i)) = 6 Then Fld(i) = "  " & Fld(i)
    If Len(Fld(i)) = 7 Then Fld(i) = " " & Fld(i)
    If Len(Fld(i)) = 8 Then Fld(i) = Fld(i)
    If Len(Fld(i)) > 8 Then Fld(i) = Left(Fld(i), 8)
Next

PutInFields = Fld(1) & Fld(2) & Fld(3) & Fld(4) & _
    Fld(5) & Fld(6) & Fld(7) & Fld(8) & Fld(9) & _
    Fld(10)

End Function
```

Flood Wave Arrival Times

A common requirement for dam and levee breach studies is to determine the time it takes after the breach occurs for flood waters to reach a certain elevation.   In some cases, investigators may wish to know when stages will reach a pre-determined flood stage, or a certain level above the bankfull stage. In either case, obtaining this data from HEC-RAS for all cross sections is a long and arduous task, as there is no direct way to publish simulation times for a specific stage. The user would have to use the profile output table and evaluate each cross section individually. For a large model with a lot of simulation time, this could take a considerable effort. HEC-RAS has options for tabulating the maximum stage for an entire reach, as well as the time to reach that maximum stage, however there is no direct option for intermediate stages.

There are two functions in the HECRASController that can easily produce a list of times for a designated stage, or increase in stage: the **Output_NodeOutput** function and the **OutputDSS_GetStageFlow** function. The **Output_NodeOutput** function retrieves the required data from the output file, so the HEC-RAS post-processor program must be run prior to calling **Output_NodeOutput**.   This is easily done by running HEC-RAS with the post-processor option turned "on" prior to running the HECRASController code, or by calling the **Compute_CurrentPlan** function in the code itself. A disadvantage to using **Output_NodeOutput** is the length of time it can take to run the post-processor-especially if you need to have significant accuracy in the published timing. For example, a 3-day simulation, with a post-processor detailed output interval of 5 minutes, requires HEC-RAS to produce 864 output profiles. For even a modest-sized model, this could take a long time.   However, if you only plan to run HEC-RAS once with the post-processor turned on, it may not be a considerable burden to the user. Further consideration should be given to the desired accuracy. With a 5 minute detailed output interval, the time to reach a specified stage will only have precision to 5 minutes.

The **OutputDSS_GetStageFlow** function retrieves stages and flows directly from the DSS file. That file is updated at the end of the unsteady flow simulation and before post-processing. Therefore, post-processing and the resulting detailed output file is not required to use **OutputDSS_GetStageFlow**. Additionally, setting your hydrograph output interval to its smallest setting, 1 minute, does not add noticeable simulation time in most models. This will allow the user to not only bypass the post-processing operation, but can get precision of reported times down to 1 minute. One disadvantage of retrieving output from the DSS file is that the user can only get stages and flow for each hydrograph output interval, versus the multitude of output parameters available from the output file (see Appendix E). But in this example, only stages are required, so using the **OutputDSS_GetStageFlow** is fine. Another warning: when retrieving output from the DSS file, HEC-RAS will only write stages and flows for cross sections at internal and external boundaries: at the ends of reaches and adjacent to structures such as bridges, inline structures, and lateral structures. This can easily be remedied by selecting more stage and flow output locations from the Options menu in the Unsteady Flow Analysis Window.

The following example code searches the output file of the Bald Eagle Dam Break data set and determines the date and time at which an increase in stage over initial conditions reaches 40 ft. It is assumed for the purpose of demonstration that 40 ft is a critical flood stage downstream of the dam that fails. Other applications may require a given incremental increase in stage over the floodplain elevation, or maybe an incremental stage above the FEMA base flood elevation. In any case, the example code could be easily adjusted to accommodate those requirements.

The **Output_NodeOutput** function is demonstrated first. As with most HECRASController programs, first instantiate a new HECRASController, then open the HEC-RAS project. Since output data is required, the code also runs the current plan.

```
Sub TimeToStages()

    '*************************************************************
    'Written by Christopher Goodell
    'Jan 24, 2014

    'Demonstrates retrieval of dates/times when a specified _
        incremental increase in stage is met.  Uses the _
        output file and the Output_NodeOutput function.  Need _
        to have a small detailed output interval to have _
```

```
      adequate resolution.  ***Caution, with a small _
      detailed output interval, this could take a long time _
      to run.

'Tested with the BaldeagleDamBrk.prj data set.
'*********************************************************

'Open the HEC-RAS project
Dim RC As New RAS500.HECRASController
Dim strProjectFileName As String
strProjectFileName = "C:\AutomateHECRAS\Unsteady " & _
      "Examples\BaldEagleDamBrk.prj"
RC.Project_Open strProjectFileName

'Run HEC-RAS
Dim blnDidItCompute As Boolean
Dim lngNumMsg As Long
Dim strMsg() As String
blnDidItCompute = RC.Compute_CurrentPlan(lngNumMsg, strMsg())
```

The next step is to set up arrays indexed to the number of cross sections that will contain the output data. The index numbers represent cross sections, numbered from downstream to upstream and arrays will be defined for River Stations, initial stages, stages for a 40 ft incremental rise, and the date/time at which the 40 ft incremental rise was met. Populating the River Station array, **strRS()**, requires the **Geometry_GetNodes** subroutine. The river and reach arguments (positions 1 and 2 in the list of parameters) are ID numbers (not string "names"), and since there is only one river and one reach in this model, long values of 1 and 1 are included as the arguments. The node type argument is also a required parameter, although it is not used in this code. Obtaining the initial stage for every cross section requires our first call to the **Output_NodeOutput** function, but simply retrieves the first real profile water surface elevation.

```
RC.Output_NodeOutput( 1, 1, i, 0, 2, lngNVar)
   Output_NodeOutput(riv As Long, rch As Long, n As Long, updn As Long, prof As Long, nVar As Long) As Single
```

Notice that the **Output_NodeOutput** function calls profile number 2. That is because profile number 1 in the output file is reserved for the MaxWS profile, which we're not interested in. Profile number 2 is actually the first real simulated profile. The river and reach (**riv**, **rch**) are ID numbers 1 and 1, and n represents the node number. The argument updn is only applicable for bridges, so it is set to 0 for this call. The Variable ID number (**nVar**) for water surface elevation is 2 (see Appendix E). A **For-Next** loop is used to retrieve initial stages for each cross section in the model.

```
'Determine the number of RS's in River 1 and Reach 1
Dim lngNumRS As Long
lngNumRS = RC.Geometry.nNode(1, 1)

'Get River Stations
Dim strRS() As String
Dim strNodeType() As String
RC.Geometry_GetNodes 1, 1, lngNumRS, strRS(), strNodeType()

'Get initial stages.  Uses profile number 2, since profile
'    number 1 is the MaxWS profile.
Dim sngInitStage() As Single: ReDim sngInitStage(1 To _
    lngNumRS)
Dim lngNVar As Long
Dim i As Long, j As Long
lngNVar = 2 'Output ID # for W/S Elevation
For i = 1 To lngNumRS
    Application.StatusBar = "Getting initial stage " & _
        "for node ID " & i & "."
    sngInitStage(i) = RC.Output_NodeOutput(1, 1, i, 0, 2, _
        lngNVar)
Next i
```

The next block of code sets up a **For-Next** loop that searches each profile in the output file for water surface elevations that first exceed 40 ft above the initial stage for each cross section.   First, an array of profile names is determined by calling the **Output_GetProfiles** subroutine. A temporary stage variable is then set up (**sngTmpStage**) to compare the stage at a given profile to the initial stage. Once that temporary stage value just exceeds 40 ft above the initial stage, the **sngStageTo40()** array is updated for the current cross section and the **strTimeTo40()** array is updated with the associated profile name. Two **For-Next** Loops are required here: one to loop through the cross sections, the other one to loop through the profiles for each cross section.

```
'Determine the number of profiles
Dim lngNumProf As Long
Dim strProfileName() As String
RC.Output_GetProfiles lngNumProf, strProfileName()

'Go through each cross section and determine the profile
'    for a stage increase of 40 feet
Dim sngTmpStage As Single
Dim sngStageTo40() As Single: ReDim sngStageTo40(1 To _
    lngNumRS)
Dim strTimeTo40() As String: ReDim strTimeTo40(1 To _
    lngNumRS)
For i = 1 To lngNumRS
    For j = 2 To lngNumProf
        Application.StatusBar = "Determining profiles " & _
            "incremental increase of 40 ft. River " & _
```

```
            "Station " & i & "of " & lngNumRS & ", " & _
            "Profile " & j & "."
        sngTmpStage = RC.Output_NodeOutput(1, 1, i, 0, _
            j, 2)
        If sngTmpStage > sngInitStage(i) + 40 Then
            sngStageTo40(i) = sngTmpStage
            strTimeTo40(i) = strProfileName(j)
            Exit For
        End If
    Next j
Next i
```

Once the **sngStageTo40()** and **strTimeTo40()** arrays are fully populated, they can be tabulated on a spreadsheet. The code first checks to see if the worksheet we'll add data to ("TimeTo40ftOutput") already exists. If it doesn't, the code creates a new one. The code then clears the sheet, adds a title and column headers, loops through the arrays and tabulates river stations, initial stages, first stage over 40 ft above initial stage, and the date/time that it occurred.

```
'First check to see if the worksheet "TimeTo40ftOutput"
'   already exists.  If not, add a new sheet and name it.
Dim blnSheetExists As Boolean
For i = 1 To Sheets.Count
    If Sheets(i).Name = "TimeTo40ftOutput" Then
        blnSheetExists = True
    End If
Next i

'If "TimeTo40ftOutput" does not exist as a sheet, we'll
'   add it.
If blnSheetExists = False Then
    Sheets.Add
    ActiveSheet.Name = "TimeTo40ftOutput"
End If
Sheets("TimeTo40ftOutput").Select

'Clear all the data so that can construct a fresh table _
    of data.
Cells.Select
Cells.Delete

'Give the sheet a title.
Range("A1").Select
ActiveCell.Value = "Time to Stage Increase of 40 ft " & _
    "using Output."

'Populate the table headers.
Range("A3") = "River": Range("A4") = "Station"
Range("B3") = "Initial": Range("B4") = "WS El (ft)"
Range("C3") = "40 ft Rise": Range("C4") = "WS El (ft)"
Range("D3") = "Date Time of": Range("D4") = "40 ft Rise"
```

There may be some cross sections that do not reach a stage increase of 40 ft, most notably upstream of the dam. When a stage value over 40 ft cannot be determined, the array indices for that cross section are left undefined with a value of 3.4E+38. So the code performs a check on the values in the **sngStageTo40()** array, and only values that are less than 10,000,000,000 will be added to the table. *Table 6* shows a portion of the table that is created from the **TimeToStages** subroutine. Notice that River Station 74000 returns an undefined single value of 3.4E+38. That's because River Station 74000 is a lateral structure that doesn't have a single water surface elevation associated with it in the output file. Also, because the **TimeToStages** subroutine reads the output file, and the Bald Eagle Dam Break model only writes detailed output every 5 minutes, the time of rise presented in the table will only show to the nearest 5 minutes. More accuracy requires either decreasing the detailed output interval, which could significantly slow down postprocessing speeds, or reading from the DSS file using the **OutputDSS_GetStageFlow** function.

```
'Loop through the HEC-RAS results arrays and populate the _
        spreadsheet.  Water surface values are rounded to 2 _
        decimal places.
    Range("A5").Select
    For i = 1 To lngNumRS
        ActiveCell.Value = strRS(i)
        ActiveCell.Offset(0, 1).Activate
        ActiveCell.Value = Round(sngInitStage(i), 2)
        ActiveCell.Offset(0, 1).Activate
        'If no 40 ft stage was determined, leave blank
        If Not sngStageTo40(i) > 10000000000# Then
            ActiveCell.Value = Round(sngStageTo40(i), 2)
            ActiveCell.Offset(0, 1).Activate
            ActiveCell.Value = strTimeTo40(i)
            ActiveCell.Offset(1, -3).Activate
        Else
            ActiveCell.Offset(1, -2).Activate
        End If
    Next i

    'Finish
    MsgBox "Done!"
    Application.StatusBar = "Finished!"
    RC.QuitRAS

End Sub
```

*Table 6. Tabulated Output using **Output_NodeOutput** function.*

Time to Stage Increase of 40 ft using Output.			
River Station	Initial WS El (ft)	40 ft Rise WS El (ft)	Date Time of 40 ft Rise
77815	585.6	627.14	03JAN1999 0245
77379	585.09	627.37	03JAN1999 0245
76865	584.42	624.43	03JAN1999 0240
75908	583.16	623.58	03JAN1999 0245
74651	581.45	621.46	03JAN1999 0315
74120	580.96	621.18	03JAN1999 0325
74000	3.4E+38	0	
73035	580.11	620.11	03JAN1999 0315
72156	579.32	619.89	03JAN1999 0315
71394	578.48	618.85	03JAN1999 0310
70531	577.63	618.58	03JAN1999 0310
69539	576.9	617.06	03JAN1999 0305

The **TimeToStages** example subroutine is presented in entirety below:

```
Sub TimeToStages()

    '*********************************************************
    'Written by Christopher Goodell
    'Jan 24, 2014

    'Demonstrates retrieval of dates/times when a specified _
        incremental increase in stage is met.  Uses the _
        output file and the Output_NodeOutput function.  Need _
        to have a small detailed output interval to have _
        adequate resolution.  ***Caution, with a small _
        detailed output interval, this could take a long time _
        to run.

    'Tested with the BaldeagleDamBrk.prj data set.
    '*********************************************************

    'Open the HEC-RAS project
    Dim RC As New RAS500.HECRASController
    Dim strProjectFileName As String
    strProjectFileName = "C:\AutomateHECRAS\Unsteady " & _
        "Examples\BaldEagleDamBrk.prj"
    RC.Project_Open strProjectFileName

    'Run HEC-RAS
    Dim blnDidItCompute As Boolean
    Dim lngNumMsg As Long
    Dim strMsg() As String
```

```
blnDidItCompute = RC.Compute_CurrentPlan(lngNumMsg, strMsg())

'Determine the number of RS's in River 1 and Reach 1
Dim lngNumRS As Long
lngNumRS = RC.Geometry.nNode(1, 1)

'Get River Stations
Dim strRS() As String
Dim strNodeType() As String
RC.Geometry_GetNodes 1, 1, lngNumRS, strRS(), strNodeType()

'Get initial stages.  Uses profile number 2, since profile
'    number 1 is the MaxWS profile.
Dim sngInitStage() As Single: ReDim sngInitStage(1 To _
    lngNumRS)
Dim lngNVar As Long
Dim i As Long, j As Long
lngNVar = 2 'Output ID # for W/S Elevation
For i = 1 To lngNumRS
    Application.StatusBar = "Getting initial stage " & _
        "for node ID " & i & "."
    sngInitStage(i) = RC.Output_NodeOutput(1, 1, i, 0, 2, _
        lngNVar)
Next i


'Determine the number of profiles
Dim lngNumProf As Long
Dim strProfileName() As String
RC.Output_GetProfiles lngNumProf, strProfileName()

'Go through each cross section and determine the profile
'    for a stage increase of 40 feet
Dim sngTmpStage As Single
Dim sngStageTo40() As Single: ReDim sngStageTo40(1 To _
    lngNumRS)
Dim strTimeTo40() As String: ReDim strTimeTo40(1 To _
    lngNumRS)
For i = 1 To lngNumRS
    For j = 2 To lngNumProf
        Application.StatusBar = "Determining profiles " & _
            "incremental increase of 40 ft. River " & _
            "Station " & i & "of " & lngNumRS & ", " & _
            "Profile " & j & "."
        sngTmpStage = RC.Output_NodeOutput(1, 1, i, 0, _
            j, 2)
        If sngTmpStage > sngInitStage(i) + 40 Then
            sngStageTo40(i) = sngTmpStage
            strTimeTo40(i) = strProfileName(j)
            Exit For
        End If
    Next j
Next i

'First check to see if the worksheet "TimeTo40ftOutput"
'    already exists.  If not, add a new sheet and name it.
Dim blnSheetExists As Boolean
```

```
    For i = 1 To Sheets.Count
        If Sheets(i).Name = "TimeTo40ftOutput" Then
            blnSheetExists = True
        End If
    Next i

    'If "TimeTo40ftOutput" does not exist as a sheet, we'll
    '   add it.
    If blnSheetExists = False Then
        Sheets.Add
        ActiveSheet.Name = "TimeTo40ftOutput"
    End If
    Sheets("TimeTo40ftOutput").Select

    'Clear all the data so that can construct a fresh table _
        of data.
    Cells.Select
    Cells.Delete

    'Give the sheet a title.
    Range("A1").Select
    ActiveCell.Value = "Time to Stage Increase of 40 ft " & _
        "using Output."

    'Populate the table headers.
    Range("A3") = "River": Range("A4") = "Station"
    Range("B3") = "Initial": Range("B4") = "WS El (ft)"
    Range("C3") = "40 ft Rise": Range("C4") = "WS El (ft)"
    Range("D3") = "Date Time of": Range("D4") = "40 ft Rise"

    'Loop through the HEC-RAS results arrays and populate the _
        spreadsheet.  Water surface values are rounded to 2 _
        decimal places.
    Range("A5").Select
    For i = 1 To lngNumRS
        ActiveCell.Value = strRS(i)
        ActiveCell.Offset(0, 1).Activate
        ActiveCell.Value = Round(sngInitStage(i), 2)
        ActiveCell.Offset(0, 1).Activate
        'If no 40 ft stage was determined, leave blank
        If Not sngStageTo40(i) > 10000000000# Then
            ActiveCell.Value = Round(sngStageTo40(i), 2)
            ActiveCell.Offset(0, 1).Activate
            ActiveCell.Value = strTimeTo40(i)
            ActiveCell.Offset(1, -3).Activate
        Else
            ActiveCell.Offset(1, -2).Activate
        End If
    Next i

    'Finish
    MsgBox "Done!"
    Application.StatusBar = "Finished!"
    RC.QuitRAS

End Sub
```

Using the **OutputDSS_GetStageFlow** function only requires a slightly different code from the example shown above.   Perhaps the biggest difference is the fact that the **OutputDSS_GetStageFlow** function does not require post-processing, since it reads directly from the DSS file which is created at the end of the unsteady flow simulation. Also, it's important to note that the **OutputDSS_GetStageFlow** function references cross sections using string names for the river, reach, and river station, while the **Output_NodeOutput** function uses the index numbers for these components. Therefore, an intermediate step of determining the string names for the river and reach is required.

Another difference is that **OutputDSS_GetStageFlow** returns stages and flows for all of the cross sections, whereas **Output_NodeOutput** does one cross section at a time.   The entire code for retrieving date/times for a 40 ft incremental rise using the **OutputDSS_GetStageFlow** function is presented next.

```
Sub TimeToStagesDSS()

    '****************************************************
    'Written by Christopher Goodell
    'Jan 26, 2014

    'Demonstrates retrieval of dates/times when a specified _
        incremental increase in stage is met.  Uses the _
        DSS file and the OutputDSS_GetStageFlow function. _
        Do not need to post process since the output file is _
        not read.  Minimize hydrograph output interval for _
        more resolution.  ***Caution.  With a small hydraulic _
        output interval, this can take a long time to run. _
        Minimize the number of cross sections to read to _
        minimize run time.

    'Tested with the BaldeagleDamBrk.prj data set.
    '****************************************************

    'Open the HEC-RAS project
    Dim RC As New RAS500.HECRASController
    Dim strProjectFileName As String
    strProjectFileName = "C:\AutomateHECRAS\Unsteady " & _
        "Examples\BaldEagleDamBrk.prj"
    RC.Project_Open strProjectFileName

    'Run HEC-RAS
    Dim blnDidItCompute As Boolean
    Dim lngNumMsg As Long
    Dim strMsg() As String
    'Can uncheck the Post Processor in HEC-RAS since don't
```

```
'   need to retrieve output data when using the
'   OutputDSS_GetStageFlow function.
blnDidItCompute = RC.Compute_CurrentPlan(lngNumMsg, _
    strMsg())

'Determine the number of RS's in River 1 and Reach 1
Dim lngNumRS As Long
lngNumRS = RC.Geometry.nNode(1, 1)

'Get River Stations
Dim strRS() As String
Dim strNodeType() As String
RC.Geometry_GetNodes 1, 1, lngNumRS, strRS(), strNodeType()

'Determine names for river, reach
Dim lngNumRiver As Long, lngNumReach As Long
Dim strRiver() As String, strReach() As String
RC.Geometry_GetRivers lngNumRiver, strRiver()
RC.Geometry_GetReaches 1, lngNumReach, strReach()

'Get initial stages as well as the stage and time to 40 ft
'   for each cross section.  Uses the
'   OutputDSS_GetStageFlow function.
Dim sngTmpStage() As Single
Dim sngTmpFlow() As Single
Dim lngTmpHydNum As Long
Dim dblTmpDateTime() As Double
Dim strErrMsg As String
Dim sngInitStage() As Single: ReDim sngInitStage(1 To _
    lngNumRS)
Dim sngStageTo40() As Single: ReDim sngStageTo40(1 To _
    lngNumRS)
Dim strTimeTo40() As String: ReDim strTimeTo40(1 To _
    lngNumRS)
Dim i As Long, j As Long
For i = 1 To lngNumRS
    Application.StatusBar = "Getting initial stage " & _
        "for node ID " & i & "."
    'Populate the temporary date/time, stage, and flow
    '   arrays.
    blnDidItCompute = RC.OutputDSS_GetStageFlow _
        (strRiver(1), strReach(1), strRS(i), _
        lngTmpHydNum, dblTmpDateTime(), sngTmpStage(), _
        sngTmpFlow(), strErrMsg)
    'Initial stage is the first Hydraulic Output record.
    sngInitStage(i) = sngTmpStage(1)
    '
    If Not sngInitStage(i) = -902 Then
        For j = lngTmpHydNum / 2 To lngTmpHydNum
            Application.StatusBar = "Determining " & _
                "profiles for incremental increase of " & _
                "40 ft. River Station " & i & "of " & _
                lngNumRS & ", " & "Hydrograph " & _
                "Output # " & j & "."
            If sngTmpStage(j) > 40 + sngInitStage(i) Then
                sngStageTo40(i) = sngTmpStage(j)
```

```
                strTimeTo40(i) = CDate(dblTmpDateTime(j))
                Exit For
            End If
        Next j
    End If
Next i

'First check to see if the worksheet "TimeTo40ftDSS"
'   already exists.  If not, add a new sheet and name it.
Dim blnSheetExists As Boolean
For i = 1 To Sheets.Count
    If Sheets(i).Name = "TimeTo40ftDSS" Then
        blnSheetExists = True
    End If
Next i

'If "TimeTo40ftDSS" does not exist as a sheet, we'll
'   add it.
If blnSheetExists = False Then
    Sheets.Add
    ActiveSheet.Name = "TimeTo40ftDSS"
End If
Sheets("TimeTo40ftDSS").Select

'Clear all the data so that can construct a fresh table _
    of data.
Cells.Select
Cells.Delete

'Give the sheet a title.
Range("A1").Select
ActiveCell.Value = "Time to Stage Increase of 40 ft " & _
    "using DSS."

'Populate the table headers.
Range("A3") = "River": Range("A4") = "Station"
Range("B3") = "Initial": Range("B4") = "WS El (ft)"
Range("C3") = "40 ft Rise": Range("C4") = "WS El (ft)"
Range("D3") = "Date Time of": Range("D4") = "40 ft Rise"

'Loop through the HEC-RAS results arrays and populate the _
    spreadsheet.  Water surface values are rounded to 2 _
    decimal places.

Range("A5").Select
For i = 1 To lngNumRS
    ActiveCell.Value = strRS(i)
    ActiveCell.Offset(0, 1).Activate
    ActiveCell.Value = Round(sngInitStage(i), 2)
    ActiveCell.Offset(0, 1).Activate
    'If no 40 ft stage was determined, leave blank
    If Not sngStageTo40(i) > 10000000000# Then
        ActiveCell.Value = Round(sngStageTo40(i), 2)
        ActiveCell.Offset(0, 1).Activate
        ActiveCell.Value = strTimeTo40(i)
        ActiveCell.Offset(1, -3).Activate
```

115

```
    Else
        ActiveCell.Offset(1, -2).Activate
    End If
Next i

'Finish
MsgBox "Done!"
Application.StatusBar = "Finished!"
RC.QuitRAS

End Sub
```

Offtake Flows – Pausing HEC-RAS to Make Changes

Occasionally users find the need to make changes to flow data during an HEC-RAS simulation for a given time step, based on the results of a previous time step. This poses a problem since there is no way for the user to explicitly make changes to input data in the middle of a simulation and have those changes apply in real simulation time. HEC-RAS does have some built-in optimization schemes, such as elevation controlled gates, and "Navigation Dams". There's also the "Rules" boundary condition that can be applied to gates or pumps. Rules are great. They offer a lot of flexibility for automated gate and/or pump control, and the applications are near endless. However, "Rules" only apply to gates and pumps, and they are limited in what they can do and complicated to use.

Another option, and one where the applications and possibilities are limitless, is to use the HECRASController in conjunction with a restart file to effectively pause HEC-RAS simulations to make those changes. The procedure is as follows:

1. Set your simulation window to one day (or whatever increment suits your needs).

2. Set your model to create a restart file at the end of the run. This is done in the Output Options menu item under Options in the unsteady flow analysis window. Run the model once to create the first restart file, then set the unsteady flow editor to read that restart file as its initial conditions.

3. Run the one day simulation.

4. Read the output file and then make changes to the flow file based on computed results at specific output locations.

5. Repeat steps 3 and 4 for a full (multiple-day) simulation.

HEC-RAS will record flows and stages at every location of the model to the restart file so that when you rerun HEC-RAS, it doesn't start from the beginning, but rather starts where it left off at the end of the previous day. This allows you to evaluate output daily and make changes to your model accordingly. Any input in the flow file or plan file can be changed in the middle of an HEC-RAS run in this manner. Geometry data cannot be changed since any change in geometry requires a rebuilding of the restart file.

The following example demonstrates the use of the pausing technique to run a year-long simulation where the amount of lateral offtake flow is regulated by the stage at a specific location in the reach. For example, if the stage decreases below some preset target, then the offtake flow will reduce correspondingly. If it continues below a second threshold stage, then the offtake flow is again reduced. Finally, below a critical stage, offtake flows are not allowed. This may simulate the desire to keep a certain amount of baseflow in a stream for environmental considerations, or to satisfy a water-rights restriction for irrigators. Although output is read daily in this example, the offtake flows are only adjusted on a weekly basis, to give the system time to adjust to the decrease (or increase) of flow.

This application requires a little upfront work in the HEC-RAS project to facilitate the "pausing" feature. This is accomplished using a restart file and setting the simulation duration to one day. HEC-RAS will then create a copy of the flow and stages at every node in the geometry at the end of the one-day simulation. Changes can be made to the flow or plan files before the model is rerun. When the model is rerun, it uses the restart file as its initial conditions so that it can start from where it paused. To make this work, the model must first run without using the restart file for initial conditions. After all, how can it use a restart file, if it hasn't been created yet? This first run should direct HEC-RAS to write the restart file by going into the Output Options of the Unsteady Flow Analysis window and checking the box that says "Write Initial Condition file at the end of the simulation" (Figure 35). Note that HEC-RAS uses the terms "Restart File", "Initial Condition File", and "Hot Start File" interchangeably. They all mean exactly the same thing.

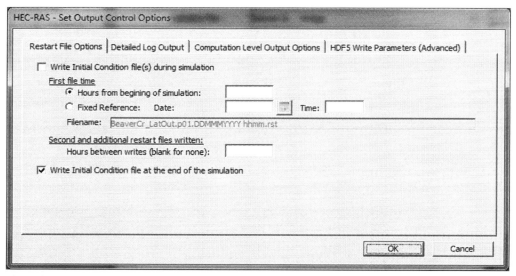

Figure 35. Output Options window.

Run HEC-RAS for one day so that the restart file can be created. Finally, set the unsteady flow, initial conditions to read the restart file that was just created (Figure 36). The model should be prepped and ready to run from the following application. This example uses a modified version of the Beaver Cr. –unsteady flow example project called "BeaverCr_LatOut.prj".

Starting with the beaver.prj dataset, the following changes were made to effectively demonstrate the pausing technique.

1. Open the standard unsteady flow HEC-RAS dataset beaver.prj, then save project as "BeaverCr_LatOut.prj

2. In the unsteady flow analysis window, change the starting and ending dates to 01JAN2014 and 02JAN2014, respectively. Make the starting and ending times both 2400. This will create a 1 day simulation. Since we will only retrieve output at the end of each 1-day simulation, change the Detailed Output Interval to 1 Day. Now go to the Options menu item and select Output Options… Under the Restart File Options tab, check the box that says "Write Initial Condition file at the end of the simulation".

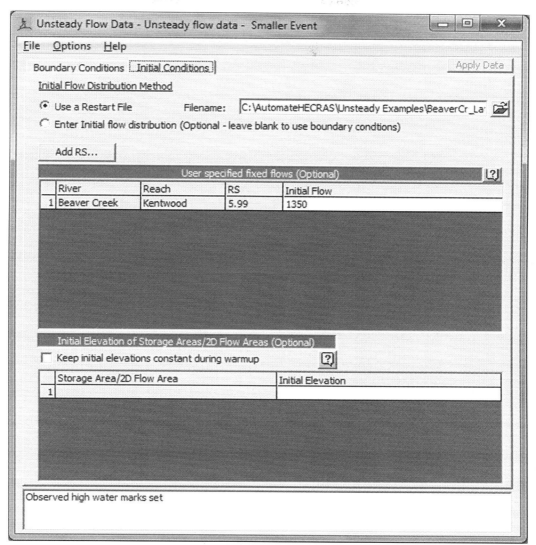

Figure 36. Using a Restart File for Initial Conditions.

3. In the unsteady flow editor, open the flow hydrograph for River Station 5.99. Change the Date time interval to 1 Day. Then change the number of ordinates (click on the No. Ordinates button) to 365. A new, 1-year long hypothetical hydrograph was inserted for River Station 5.99 as shown in Figure 37. Also, for the table dates, use a "Fixed Start Time" with a Date of 01JAN2014 and a Time of 2400. Now add a lateral inflow hydrograph at River Station 5.76. Set the Date time interval to 1 Year (the Date time interval is inconsequential, as long as it is greater than the duration of the simulation). For simulation time 00:00 (01Jan2014 2400) enter a value of 0. Do the same for simulation time 8760:00 (01Jan2015 2400).

4. Save the project and Compute the simulation. Reopen the unsteady flow editor and go to the Initial Conditions tab. Select "Use a Restart File" and browse for and select the file "BeaverCr_LatOut.p03.02JAN2014 2400.rst".

5. Compute the simulation to verify that the initial conditions file is being read. <u>Close HEC-RAS</u>.

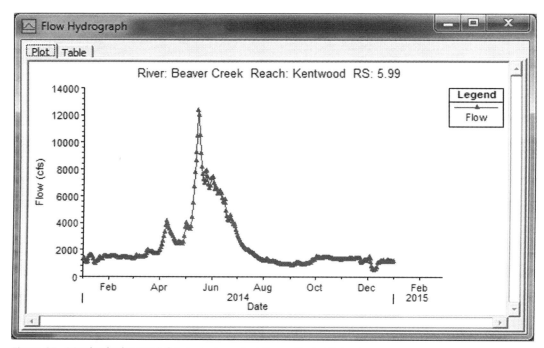

Figure 37. 365 day hydrograph for example project BeaverCr_LatOut.prj.

Now that the model is prepped, we can run a year's worth of simulation, while automatically pausing daily to read results and make adjustments to the offtake flow accordingly. This requires running the model through a subroutine that uses the HECRASController to read output and to rewrite the plan and flow files after each 1-day simulation.

The first step in writing the code is to define a new HECRASController, open the HEC-RAS project and run it. However, we can't dimension a new HECRASController in the current scope, because HEC-RAS will remain open as a process until the subroutine has completed. We'll be manipulating the flow input text file and the only way for the new input data to be read into HEC-RAS is to reopen the project. It can't be reopened if it is already open. So, to get around this, we'll call a separate subroutine, called **OpenRunCloseRAS** that will do just as the name implies. After the separate subroutine opens, runs, and closes RAS, that subroutine ends and HEC-RAS is closed as a Windows® process. Then we can return to the primary subroutine and continue on until we loop through to the next day and do it all again. The **OpenRunCloseRAS** subroutine is presented at the end of this section. Plan and flow files are also defined. Notice that in addition to the established plan and flow files, temporary versions are also set up. These temporary files will be used to write text input data to during run-time. Once the temporary files are completed, they'll be copied over the originals to be used for the next HEC-RAS simulation.

```
Sub OfftakeFlow()

    '*******************************************************
    'Demonstrates pausing of HEC-RAS to make changes to _
        offtake flows.  Also demonstrates reading and writing _
        to HEC-RAS input files.

    'Written by Christopher Goodell
    'February 3, 2014

    'This subroutine will run HEC-RAS for one day, then check _
        the results.  It then reruns HEC-RAS for another day _
        and repeats.  On every 7th day, it will change the _
        offtake flow to a hypothetical offtake canal based on _
        the water surface elevation in the river.  This _
        is done for a full year to demonstrate how offtake _
        flows can be guided by resulting water surface _
        elevations.

    'Tested with a modification to the beaver.prj data set _
        called BeaverCr_LatOut.prj.  See the description in _
        the book for modifications that were made.
    '*******************************************************

    'Open the HEC-RAS project, Run HEC-RAS and then close _
        HEC-RAS
    Dim strProjectFileName As String
    strProjectFileName = "C:\AutomateHECRAS\Unsteady " & _
        "Examples\BeaverCr_LatOut.prj"
    OpenRunCloseRAS strProjectFileName, False

    'Define the plan and flow files and temporary files to _
        write to
    Dim strPlanFile As String
    Dim strNewPlanFile As String
    Dim strFlowFile As String
    Dim strNewFlowFile As String
    strPlanFile = "C:\AutomateHECRAS\Unsteady Examples\" & _
        "BeaverCr_LatOut.p03"
    strNewPlanFile = "C:\AutomateHECRAS\Unsteady Examples\" & _
        "BeaverCr_LatOut.tempp03"
    strFlowFile = "C:\AutomateHECRAS\Unsteady Examples\" & _
        "BeaverCr_LatOut.u02"
    strNewFlowFile = "C:\AutomateHECRAS\Unsteady Examples\" & _
        "BeaverCr_LatOut.tempu02"
```

Next, the target river station is set to "5.13" and the last profile name is stored in a string variable called **strProfName**. The last profile represents the conditions at the end of each incremental day. The last profile is determined using the **GetNumProfiles** function, which calls the **Output_GetProfiles** subroutine. **GetNumProfiles** is included at the end of this section. The initial start and end date/times are also defined here. These will be adjusted by one day after each HEC-RAS simulation. An additional function was written to convert date variables to strings so that the date/times written to the plan text file is in the correct format. The **ConvertDateToString** function is included at the end of this section.

```
'Get node ID number
Dim lngNodeID As Long
Dim lngRiv As Long, lngRch As Long, strNode As String
    'Get from first river and first reach, node "5.13"
lngRiv = 1: lngRch = 1: strNode = "5.13"
lngNodeID = GetNodeID(strProjectFileName, lngRiv, lngRch, _
    strNode)

'Get last profile number
Dim lngNumProf As Long
Dim strProfName() As String
lngNumProf = GetNumProfiles(strProjectFileName, _
    strProfName())

'Set start and end dates and convert from strings to date _
    data types
Dim dteStartDate As Date, dteEndDate As Date
Dim strStartDate As String, strEndDate As String
dteStartDate = #1/1/2014#
strStartDate = mTxtReadWrite.ConvertDateToString _
    (dteStartDate)
dteEndDate = dteStartDate + 1
strEndDate = mTxtReadWrite.ConvertDateToString(dteEndDate)
```

The column headers on the output spreadsheet are populated prior to entering the Do-Loop that runs and pauses HEC-RAS for a year's worth of simulation. The Do Loop is terminated once the start date reaches January 1, 2015, exactly one year after the original start date. Inside the Do-Loop, the application retrieves the water surface elevation at the target river station. Every seven days, it determines the offtake flow based on the preset rules, records the offtake flows and stages on the spreadsheet, and sets the new lateral offtake flows in the flow file. A progress bar is also set up to provide progress updates to the user during the simulation. Retrieving the water surface elevation requires calling the **Output_NodeOutput** function. However, since we need to prevent the instantiation of a new HECRASController and opening HEC-RAS in the current scope, a separate function was written, called **GetOutputValue**. This function is presented at the end of the section. The rules indicate that if the stage at the target location is greater than or equal to 211.5 ft, then the full amount of offtake flow (4,000 cfs) is allowed. If the stage is between 211 and 211.5 ft, then 3,000 cfs can be withdrawn. If the stage is below 207.5 ft, then no offtake flows are allowed.   *Table 7* shows the complete offtake flow schedule used in this example.

Table 7. Offtake Flow Schedule

Stage (ft)	Offtake Flow (cfs)
>= 211.5	4000
>=211	3000
>=210.5	2000
>=210	1500
>=209.5	1000
>=209	800
>=208.5	600
>=208	400
>=207.5	200
< 207.5	0

```
'Populate column headers on the OfftakeOutput sheet.
Sheets("OfftakeOutput").Select
Cells(1, 1).Value = "": Cells(2, 1).Value = "Date"
Cells(1, 2).Value = "Offtake": Cells(2, 2).Value = "Flow"
Cells(1, 3).Value = "New": Cells(2, 3).Value = "Stage"
Cells(1, 4).Value = "Original": Cells(2, 4).Value = "Stage"

'Set properties on the Progress form, and Show it.
Dim frmProg As New frmProg
frmProg.progProg.Min = 0
frmProg.progProg.Max = 1000
frmProg.progProg.Value = 0
frmProg.Show (False)

'Run HEC-RAS one day at a time.  Pause HEC-RAS after one
'    day, check target water surface elevation, and then
'    change the offtake flow accordingly.  Repeat using a
'    Do-Loop for an entire calendar year.
Dim strLine As String
Dim sngWSELInitial As Single
Dim sngWSEL As Single
Dim sngQOut As Single
Dim lngUpDn As Long
Dim lngVar As Long
lngUpDn = 0 'regular cross section

Dim i As Integer, lngCount As Integer
i = 3
lngCount = 0
Do Until dteStartDate >= #1/1/2015# 'Careful...this is _
```

123

```
        USA date convention (MM/DD/YYYY)

    'Set the counter to keep track of 7th day
    lngCount = lngCount + 1

    'Get Water Surface Elevation at River Station 5.13 _
        for first profile.
    lngVar = 2 'Variable ID for Water Surface Elevation
    sngWSELInitial = GetOutputValue(strProjectFileName, _
        lngRiv, lngRch, lngNodeID, lngUpDn, 1, _
        lngVar)

    'Get Water Surface Elevation at River Station 5.13 _
        for last profile.
    sngWSEL = GetOutputValue(strProjectFileName, _
        lngRiv, lngRch, lngNodeID, lngUpDn, lngNumProf, _
        lngVar)

    'Determine new offtake flow based on target ws elev, _
        but only on the 7th day.
    If lngCount = 7 Then
        If sngWSEL >= 211.5 Then
            sngQOut = -4000
        ElseIf sngWSEL >= 211 Then
            sngQOut = -3000
        ElseIf sngWSEL >= 210.5 Then
            sngQOut = -2000
        ElseIf sngWSEL >= 210 Then
            sngQOut = -1500
        ElseIf sngWSEL >= 209.5 Then
            sngQOut = -1000
        ElseIf sngWSEL >= 209 Then
            sngQOut = -800
        ElseIf sngWSEL >= 208.5 Then
            sngQOut = -600
        ElseIf sngWSEL >= 208 Then
            sngQOut = -400
        ElseIf sngWSEL >= 207.5 Then
            sngQOut = -200
        Else
            sngQOut = 0
        End If

        'reset the counter
        lngCount = 0
    Else
        'Check to make sure withdrawls are not taken on ANY _
            day where the WSEL is less than 207.5.
        If sngWSEL < 207.5 Then
            sngQOut = 0
        End If
    End If

    'Record offtake flows and ws elevations on spreadsheet
    Cells(i, 1).Value = dteStartDate
    Cells(i, 2).Value = -1 * sngQOut
```

```
If i = 1 Then
    Cells(i, 3).Value = sngWSELInitial
Else
    Cells(i, 3).Value = sngWSEL
End If
i = i + 1
```

Setting the offtake flows in HEC-RAS requires a read/write to the unsteady flow text file. The offtake flow location is River Station 5.76, so another Do-Loop searches the flow file for the key "Boundary Location=". Once it finds the "Boundary Location" key, it checks to see if the partial string "5.76" is in that line of text, which indicates it found the correct location. The application then rewrites that line of text in the temporary flow file to include the new offtake flow, which is represented by the Single variable **sngQOut**. Once the temporary flow file is rewritten, both it and the original flow files are closed. Then the **FileCopy** and **Kill** subroutines (members of **VBA.FileSystem** class) are used to replace the original flow file with the temporary one.

```
'Set new Lateral Offtake flows
Open strFlowFile For Input As #1
Open strNewFlowFile For Output As #2

Do While Not EOF(1)
    Line Input #1, strLine
    If InStr(strLine, "Boundary Location=Beaver " & _
            "Creek") Then
        Print #2, strLine
        If InStr(strLine, "5.76") Then
            Line Input #1, strLine: Print #2, strLine
            Line Input #1, strLine: Print #2, strLine
            Line Input #1, strLine
            Print #2, mTxtReadWrite.PutInFields _
                (sngQOut, sngQOut, "", "", "", "", _
                "", "", "", "")
        End If
    Else
        Print #2, strLine
    End If
Loop

'Close the unsteady flow text files
Close #1
Close #2

'Replace the original flow file with the _
    temporary one, then delete the temporary one.
FileCopy strNewFlowFile, strFlowFile
Kill strNewFlowFile
```

Next, the plan file is updated with a new simulation time window, representing the next day in the process. Here, the application searches the plan text file for the key "Simulation Date=". Once found, it replaces the previous date/time, with the new one

(one day later). The original plan file is then overwritten by the temporary one and the progress bar is updated. With a new flow file and a new plan file, HEC-RAS is reopened (so that the new plan and flow files can be read in) and rerun for the next day in the sequence by once again calling the **OpenRunCloseRAS** subroutine.

```
'Set simulation time in plan file
Open strPlanFile For Input As #1
Open strNewPlanFile For Output As #2
Do While Not EOF(1)
    Line Input #1, strLine
    If InStr(strLine, "Simulation Date=") Then
        Print #2, "Simulation Date=" & dteStartDate & _
            ",2400," & dteStartDate + 1 & ",2400"
    Else
        Print #2, strLine
    End If
Loop

'Close the plan text files
Close #1
Close #2

'Replace the original plan file with the _
    temporary one, then delete the temporary one.
FileCopy strNewPlanFile, strPlanFile
Kill strNewPlanFile

'Update Progress bar for "ith" run out of 365.
frmProg.progProg.Value = ((i - 3) / 366) * 1000
frmProg.Caption = strStartDate & ".  W/S Elev = " & _
    sngWSEL & " ft. Offtake Q = " & sngQOut & "."

'Open, ReRun, and Close HEC-RAS
OpenRunCloseRAS strProjectFileName, True
```

The restart filename is updated in the plan text file so that it is properly referenced for the next run. The application searches for the key "Restart Filename=" and replaces the old restart filename with the new one.   Once the restart filename is replaced in the plan file, the HEC-RAS project is saved, the starting and ending date/times are increased by one day and the entire process is repeated for the next simulation day.

```
'Change the restart file to use for next time
Open strFlowFile For Input As #1
Open strNewFlowFile For Output As #2

Do While Not EOF(1)
    Line Input #1, strLine
    If InStr(strLine, "Restart Filename=") Then
        'Change the restart file to use.
        Print #2, _
            "Restart Filename=BeaverCr_LatOut.p03." _
```

```
                              & strEndDate & " 2400.rst"
                              'Get rid of the old restart file
                              If dteStartDate > #1/2/2014# Then
                                  Kill strPlanFile & "." & _
                                      strStartDate & " 2400.rst"
                              End If
                      Else
                          Print #2, strLine
                      End If
              Loop

              'Close the unsteady flow text files
              Close #1
              Close #2

              'Replace the original flow file with the _
                  temporary one, then delete the temporary one.
              FileCopy strNewFlowFile, strFlowFile
              Kill strNewFlowFile

              'Set new dates and get string versions
              dteStartDate = dteStartDate + 1
              strStartDate = mTxtReadWrite.ConvertDateToString _
                  (dteStartDate)
              dteEndDate = dteStartDate + 1
              strEndDate = mTxtReadWrite.ConvertDateToString _
                  (dteEndDate)

      Loop
```

After looping through each one-day simulation for a full 365 days, the flow file and plan file are reset to their original states and the application is complete.

```
      'Reset flow file to initial settings.
      frmProg.Caption = "Resetting Files..."
      Open strFlowFile For Input As #1
      Open strNewFlowFile For Output As #2

      Do While Not EOF(1)
          Line Input #1, strLine
          If InStr(strLine, "Restart Filename=") Then
              'Change the restart file to use.
              Print #2, _
                  "Restart Filename=BeaverCr_LatOut.p01." & _
                      "02JAN2014 2400.rst"
          ElseIf InStr(strLine, "Boundary Location=Beaver " & _
              "Creek") Then
              Print #2, strLine
              If InStr(strLine, "5.76") Then
                  Line Input #1, strLine: Print #2, strLine
                  Line Input #1, strLine: Print #2, strLine
                  Line Input #1, strLine
                  Print #2, mTxtReadWrite.PutInFields _
                      (0, 0, "", "", "", "", _
                          "", "", "", "")
```

```
                End If
        Else
              Print #2, strLine
        End If
    Loop

    'Close the unsteady flow text files
    Close #1
    Close #2

    'Replace the original flow file with the _
            temporary one, then delete the temporary one.
    FileCopy strNewFlowFile, strFlowFile
    Kill strNewFlowFile


    'Reset plan file to initial settings.
    Open strPlanFile For Input As #1
    Open strNewPlanFile For Output As #2
    Do While Not EOF(1)
        Line Input #1, strLine
        If InStr(strLine, "Simulation Date=") Then
            Print #2, "Simulation Date=1/1/2014,2400," & _
                "1/2/2014,2400"
        Else
              Print #2, strLine
        End If
    Loop

    'Close the plan text files
    Close #1
    Close #2

    'Replace the original plan file with the _
            temporary one, then delete the temporary one.
    FileCopy strNewPlanFile, strPlanFile
    Kill strNewPlanFile

    frmProg.Caption = "Finished!"
End Sub
```

For each day in the simulation, the offtake flow (blue line) and the new stage (red line) at the target location were recorded on the spreadsheet. The original stage from a previous simulation (without offtake flows) is included as well for comparison (green line). The results were plotted for visualization (Figure 38). Offtake withdrawals are allowed through much of the year, except for a period in the late summer months where stages dip below the threshold elevation of 207.5 ft. There's also a brief drought period during the first half of December where offtake flows are not allowed. During the spring and early summer snowmelt period, inflows to Beaver Creek increase dramatically, and the full offtake allotment of 4,000 cfs is allowed briefly during the month of May.

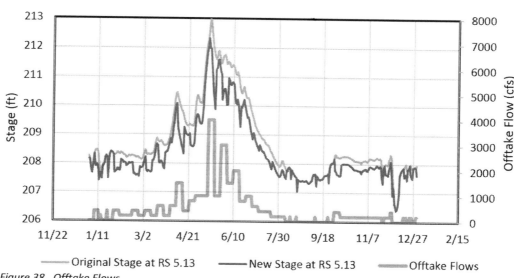

Figure 38. Offtake Flows.

The complete code for this application is presented below.

```
Sub OfftakeFlow()

'******************************************************
'Demonstrates pausing of HEC-RAS to make changes to _
    offtake flows.  Also demonstrates reading and writing _
    to HEC-RAS input files

'Written by Christopher Goodell
'February 3, 2014

'This subroutine will run HEC-RAS for one day, then check _
    the results.  It then reruns HEC-RAS for another day _
    and repeats.  On every 7th day, it will change the _
    offtake flow to a hypothetical offtake canal based on _
    the water surface elevation in the river.  This _
    is done for a full year to demonstrate how offtake _
    flows can be guided by resulting water surface _
    elevations.

'Tested with a modification to the beaver.prj data set _
    called BeaverCr_LatOut.prj.  See the description in _
    the book for modifications that were made.
'******************************************************

'Open the HEC-RAS project, Run HEC-RAS and then close _
    HEC-RAS
Dim strProjectFileName As String
strProjectFileName = "C:\AutomateHECRAS\Unsteady " & _
    "Examples\BeaverCr_LatOut.prj"
OpenRunCloseRAS strProjectFileName, False

'Define the plan and flow files and temporary files to _
```

```
        write to
Dim strPlanFile As String
Dim strNewPlanFile As String
Dim strFlowFile As String
Dim strNewFlowFile As String
strPlanFile = "C:\AutomateHECRAS\Unsteady Examples\" & _
    "BeaverCr_LatOut.p03"
strNewPlanFile = "C:\AutomateHECRAS\Unsteady Examples\" & _
    "BeaverCr_LatOut.tempp03"
strFlowFile = "C:\AutomateHECRAS\Unsteady Examples\" & _
    "BeaverCr_LatOut.u02"
strNewFlowFile = "C:\AutomateHECRAS\Unsteady Examples\" & _
    "BeaverCr_LatOut.tempu02"

'Get node ID number
Dim lngNodeID As Long
Dim lngRiv As Long, lngRch As Long, strNode As String
    'Get from first river and first reach, node "5.13"
lngRiv = 1: lngRch = 1: strNode = "5.13"
lngNodeID = GetNodeID(strProjectFileName, lngRiv, lngRch, _
    strNode)

'Get last profile number
Dim lngNumProf As Long
Dim strProfName() As String
lngNumProf = GetNumProfiles(strProjectFileName, _
    strProfName())

'Set start and end dates and convert from strings to date _
    data types
Dim dteStartDate As Date, dteEndDate As Date
Dim strStartDate As String, strEndDate As String
dteStartDate = #1/1/2014#
strStartDate = mTxtReadWrite.ConvertDateToString _
    (dteStartDate)
dteEndDate = dteStartDate + 1
strEndDate = mTxtReadWrite.ConvertDateToString(dteEndDate)

'Populate column headers on the OfftakeOutput sheet.
Sheets("OfftakeOutput").Select
Cells(1, 1).Value = "": Cells(2, 1).Value = "Date"
Cells(1, 2).Value = "Offtake": Cells(2, 2).Value = "Flow"
Cells(1, 3).Value = "New": Cells(2, 3).Value = "Stage"
Cells(1, 4).Value = "Original": Cells(2, 4).Value = "Stage"

'Set properties on the Progress form, and Show it.
Dim frmProg As New frmProg
frmProg.progProg.Min = 0
frmProg.progProg.Max = 1000
frmProg.progProg.Value = 0
frmProg.Show (False)

'Run HEC-RAS one day at a time.  Pause HEC-RAS after one
'    day, check target water surface elevation, and then
'    change the offtake flow accordingly.  Repeat using a
'    Do-Loop for an entire calendar year.
```

```
Dim strLine As String
Dim sngWSELInitial As Single
Dim sngWSEL As Single
Dim sngQOut As Single
Dim lngUpDn As Long
Dim lngVar As Long
lngUpDn = 0 'regular cross section

Dim i As Integer, lngCount As Integer
i = 3
lngCount = 0
Do Until dteStartDate >= #1/1/2015# 'Careful...this is _
    USA date convention (MM/DD/YYYY)

    'Set the counter to keep track of 7th day
    lngCount = lngCount + 1

    'Get Water Surface Elevation at River Station 5.13 _
        for first profile.
    lngVar = 2 'Variable ID for Water Surface Elevation
    sngWSELInitial = GetOutputValue(strProjectFileName, _
        lngRiv, lngRch, lngNodeID, lngUpDn, 1, _
        lngVar)

    'Get Water Surface Elevation at River Station 5.13 _
        for last profile.
    sngWSEL = GetOutputValue(strProjectFileName, _
        lngRiv, lngRch, lngNodeID, lngUpDn, lngNumProf, _
        lngVar)

    'Determine new offtake flow based on target ws elev, _
        but only on the 7th day.
    If lngCount = 7 Then
        If sngWSEL >= 211.5 Then
            sngQOut = -4000
        ElseIf sngWSEL >= 211 Then
            sngQOut = -3000
        ElseIf sngWSEL >= 210.5 Then
            sngQOut = -2000
        ElseIf sngWSEL >= 210 Then
            sngQOut = -1500
        ElseIf sngWSEL >= 209.5 Then
            sngQOut = -1000
        ElseIf sngWSEL >= 209 Then
            sngQOut = -800
        ElseIf sngWSEL >= 208.5 Then
            sngQOut = -600
        ElseIf sngWSEL >= 208 Then
            sngQOut = -400
        ElseIf sngWSEL >= 207.5 Then
            sngQOut = -200
        Else
            sngQOut = 0
        End If

        'reset the counter
```

131

```
            lngCount = 0
    Else
        'Check to make sure withdrawls are not taken on ANY _
            day where the WSEL is less than 207.5.
        If sngWSEL < 207.5 Then
            sngQOut = 0
        End If
    End If

    'Record offtake flows and ws elevations on spreadsheet
    Cells(i, 1).Value = dteStartDate
    Cells(i, 2).Value = -1 * sngQOut
    If i = 1 Then
        Cells(i, 3).Value = sngWSELInitial
    Else
        Cells(i, 3).Value = sngWSEL
    End If
    i = i + 1

    'Set new Lateral Offtake flows
    Open strFlowFile For Input As #1
    Open strNewFlowFile For Output As #2

    Do While Not EOF(1)
        Line Input #1, strLine
        If InStr(strLine, "Boundary Location=Beaver " & _
                "Creek") Then
            Print #2, strLine
            If InStr(strLine, "5.76") Then
                Line Input #1, strLine: Print #2, strLine
                Line Input #1, strLine: Print #2, strLine
                Line Input #1, strLine
                Print #2, mTxtReadWrite.PutInFields _
                    (sngQOut, sngQOut, "", "", "", "", _
                        "", "", "", "")
            End If
        Else
            Print #2, strLine
        End If
    Loop

    'Close the unsteady flow text files
    Close #1
    Close #2

    'Replace the original flow file with the _
        temporary one, then delete the temporary one.
    FileCopy strNewFlowFile, strFlowFile
    Kill strNewFlowFile

    'Set simulation time in plan file
    Open strPlanFile For Input As #1
    Open strNewPlanFile For Output As #2
    Do While Not EOF(1)
        Line Input #1, strLine
        If InStr(strLine, "Simulation Date=") Then
```

```
            Print #2, "Simulation Date=" & dteStartDate & _
                ",2400," & dteStartDate + 1 & ",2400"
        Else
            Print #2, strLine
        End If
Loop

'Close the plan text files
Close #1
Close #2

'Replace the original plan file with the _
    temporary one, then delete the temporary one.
FileCopy strNewPlanFile, strPlanFile
Kill strNewPlanFile

'Update Progress bar for "ith" run out of 365.
frmProg.progProg.Value = ((i - 3) / 366) * 1000
frmProg.Caption = strStartDate & ".  W/S Elev = " & _
    sngWSEL & " ft. Offtake Q = " & sngQOut & "."

'Open, ReRun, and Close HEC-RAS
OpenRunCloseRAS strProjectFileName, True

'Change the restart file to use for next time
Open strFlowFile For Input As #1
Open strNewFlowFile For Output As #2

Do While Not EOF(1)
    Line Input #1, strLine
    If InStr(strLine, "Restart Filename=") Then
        'Change the restart file to use.
        Print #2, _
            "Restart Filename=BeaverCr_LatOut.p03." _
            & strEndDate & " 2400.rst"
            'Get rid of the old restart file
            If dteStartDate > #1/2/2014# Then
                Kill strPlanFile & "." & _
                    strStartDate & " 2400.rst"
            End If
    Else
        Print #2, strLine
    End If
Loop

'Close the unsteady flow text files
Close #1
Close #2

'Replace the original flow file with the _
    temporary one, then delete the temporary one.
FileCopy strNewFlowFile, strFlowFile
Kill strNewFlowFile

'Set new dates and get string versions
dteStartDate = dteStartDate + 1
```

```
    strStartDate = mTxtReadWrite.ConvertDateToString _
        (dteStartDate)
    dteEndDate = dteStartDate + 1
    strEndDate = mTxtReadWrite.ConvertDateToString _
        (dteEndDate)

Loop

'Reset flow file to initial settings.
frmProg.Caption = "Resetting Files..."
Open strFlowFile For Input As #1
Open strNewFlowFile For Output As #2

Do While Not EOF(1)
    Line Input #1, strLine
    If InStr(strLine, "Restart Filename=") Then
        'Change the restart file to use.
        Print #2, _
            "Restart Filename=BeaverCr_LatOut.p01." & _
                "02JAN2014 2400.rst"
    ElseIf InStr(strLine, "Boundary Location=Beaver " & _
            "Creek") Then
        Print #2, strLine
        If InStr(strLine, "5.76") Then
            Line Input #1, strLine: Print #2, strLine
            Line Input #1, strLine: Print #2, strLine
            Line Input #1, strLine
            Print #2, mTxtReadWrite.PutInFields _
                (0, 0, "", "", "", "", _
                    "", "", "", "")
        End If
    Else
        Print #2, strLine
    End If
Loop

'Close the unsteady flow text files
Close #1
Close #2

'Replace the original flow file with the _
        temporary one, then delete the temporary one.
FileCopy strNewFlowFile, strFlowFile
Kill strNewFlowFile


'Reset plan file to initial settings.
Open strPlanFile For Input As #1
Open strNewPlanFile For Output As #2
Do While Not EOF(1)
    Line Input #1, strLine
    If InStr(strLine, "Simulation Date=") Then
        Print #2, "Simulation Date=1/1/2014,2400," & _
            "1/2/2014,2400"
    Else
        Print #2, strLine
```

```
        End If
    Loop

    'Close the plan text files
    Close #1
    Close #2

    'Replace the original plan file with the _
         temporary one, then delete the temporary one.
    FileCopy strNewPlanFile, strPlanFile
    Kill strNewPlanFile

    frmProg.Caption = "Finished!"
End Sub
```

The following procedures are called by the subroutine OfftakeFlows:

```
Sub OpenRunCloseRAS(RASProject As String, HideRAS As Boolean)

    '*********************************************************
    'Demonstrates Project_Open subroutine and the _
        Compute_CurrentPlan function.

    'Written by Christopher Goodell
    'August 26, 2014
    '*********************************************************

    'Open HEC-RAS
    Dim RC As New HECRASController
    RC.Project_Open RASProject

    'Run HEC-RAS
    Dim blnDidItCompute As Boolean, lngMsg As Long, _
        strMsg() As String
    If HideRAS Then RC.Compute_HideComputationWindow
    blnDidItCompute = RC.Compute_CurrentPlan(lngMsg, strMsg())

    'Close HEC-RAS
    RC.QuitRAS

End Sub

Function GetNodeID(RASProject As String, lngRiv As Long, _
    lngRch As Long, strNode As String) As Long

    '*********************************************************
    'Demonstrates the Output_NodeID function.

    'Written by Christopher Goodell
    'August 26, 2014

    'Gets the node ID number for a given node name.
    '*********************************************************

    'Open HEC-RAS
    Dim RC As New HECRASController
```

135

```
    RC.Project_Open RASProject

    'Get Node ID
    GetNodeID = RC.Output_GetNode(lngRiv, lngRch, strNode)

    'Close HEC-RAS
    RC.QuitRAS

End Function

Function GetNumProfiles(RASProject As String, _
    ByRef strProfiles() As String) As Long

    '***********************************************************
    'Demonstrates the Output_GetProfiles subroutine.

    'Written by Christopher Goodell
    'August 26, 2014

    'Gets the number of profiles and array of profile names.
    '***********************************************************

    'Open HEC-RAS
    Dim RC As New HECRASController
    RC.Project_Open RASProject

    'Get Profiles
    Dim lngProf As Long
    RC.Output_GetProfiles lngProf, strProfiles()
    GetNumProfiles = lngProf

    'Close HEC-RAS
    RC.QuitRAS

End Function




Function GetOutputValue(RASProject As String, lngRiv As Long, _
    lngRch As Long, lngNode As Long, lngUpDn As Long, _
    lngProf As Long, lngVar As Long)

    '***********************************************************
    'Demonstrates the Output_NodeOutput function.

    'Written by Christopher Goodell
    'August 26, 2014

    'Gets an output value from the output file.
    '***********************************************************

    'Open HEC-RAS
    Dim RC As New HECRASController
    RC.Project_Open RASProject
```

```
'Get Output
GetOutputValue = RC.Output_NodeOutput(lngRiv, lngRch, _
    lngNode, lngUpDn, lngProf, lngVar)

'Close HEC-RAS
RC.QuitRAS

End Function
```

APPENDIX A.

THE HEC-RAS DYNAMIC LINK LIBRARY

HECRASController Class

Compute_Complete

Returns a true value once computations have completed.

Type: Function   **Category**: Info

Notes: Can be called during computations if Blocking Mode in Compute_CurrentPlan is set to false.

Arguments: None.

Compute_CurrentPlan

Computes the current plan.

Type: Function **Category**: Action **Returns**: True or False
(Boolean)

Notes: Returns true, if the computation worked properly, false if not.

Arguments: **nmsg** (long), the number of returned messages

msg() (string), messages returned from HECRASController during computations.

BlockingMode (boolean, optional), True or false. If Blocking Mode is set to False, then code will continue to be read while HEC-RAS is computing. Otherwise, run-time will be paused. By default, the HECRASController sets blocking mode to "True".

Compute_HideComputationWindow

Sets the computation window to be hidden during computations.

Type: Subroutine **Category**: Action

Notes: This should be called before Compute_CurrentPlan.

Arguments: None.

Compute_ShowComputationWindow

Sets the computation window to be visible during computations.

Type: Subroutine **Category**: Action

Notes: This should be called before Compute_CurrentPlan. Because by default the RAS Controller shows the Computation Window, this is not necessary unless the Computation Window was already hidden in a previous line of code.

Arguments: None.

Compute_WATPlan

Computes a WAT plan.

Type: Function   **Category**: Action   **Returns**: True or False
(Boolean)

Notes: For WAT only.

Arguments: None.

ComputeProgressBar

Repeatedly returns a single value between 0 and 1, indicating the progress of the computations.

Type: Event   **Category**: Info

Notes: Must instantiate the HECRASController "With Events" in a class module or in a sheet.   Then the event XX.ComputeProgressBar becomes available for code. XX being the variable name for the instantiated HECRASController. XX_ComputeProgressBar is called repeatedly once Compute_CurrentPlan is called and through the duration of the HEC-RAS Computations.

Arguments: **Progress** (single), progress of computations [0,1].

ComputeProgressMessage

Repeatedly returns the computation messages during computations.

Type: Event   **Category**: Info

Notes: Must instantiate the HECRASController "With Events" in a class module or in a sheet.   Then the subroutine XX_ComputeProgressMessage becomes available for code. XX being the variable name for the instantiated HECRASController. XX_ComputeProgressMessage is called repeatedly once Compute_CurrentPlan is called and through the duration of the HEC-RAS Computations.

Arguments: **Msg** (string), computation message.

ComputeStartedFromController

Indicates if computations started from HECRASController.

Type: Property   **Category**: Info   **Returns**: True or False

Notes: Must set BlockingMode to false in the Compute_CurrentPlan function for this to work.

Arguments: None.

Create_WATPlanName

Returns a WAT Plan Name, based on the RAS base plan name and the simulation name.

Type: Function   **Category**: Action   **Returns**: String

Notes: For WAT only.

Arguments: **HECRASBasePlanName** (string)

SimulationName (string)

CurrentGeomFile

Indicates the current HEC-RAS geometry file and its path.

Type: Function   **Category**: Info   **Returns**: The current Geometry File (string)

Notes:

Arguments: None

CurrentPlanFile

Indicates the current HEC-RAS plan file and its path.

Type: Function   **Category**: Info   **Returns**: The current Plan File (string).

Notes:

Arguments: None

CurrentProjectFile

Indicates the current HEC-RAS project file and its path.

Type: Function   **Category**: Info   **Returns**: The current project
file (string)

Notes:

Arguments: None

CurrentProjectTitle

Indicates the current HEC-RAS project title.

Type: Function   **Category**: Info   **Returns**: The current project's
title (string)

Notes:

Arguments: None

CurrentSteadyFile

Indicates the current HEC-RAS steady flow file and path.

Type: Function   **Category**: Info   **Returns**: The current steady
flow file (string)

Notes:

Arguments: None

CurrentUnsteadyFile

Indicates the current HEC-RAS unsteady flow file and path.

Type: Function   **Category**: Info   **Returns**: The current unsteady
flow file (string)

Notes:

Arguments: None

Edit_AddBC

Adds a bridge/culvert.

Type: Subroutine   **Category**: Edit

Notes: The Edit_BC subroutine must be included in the code after Edit_AddBC, and must call the newly added bridge/culvert in order for it to be saved to the geometry file. Edit_BC brings up the Bridge/Culvert Editor. No edits are necessary to save the new bridge/culvert, the editor has to just open and close. Without Edit_BC, once the code has been completed and the HECRASController closes, HEC-RAS will close and the newly added bridge/culvert will be lost.

Arguments: **river** (string). The river name to add the bridge/culvert to.

reach (string). The reach name to add the bridge/culvert to.

rs (string). The river station of the new bridge/culvert.

errmsg (string). If an error occurs within the RAS Controller, RC Returns a string containing a description of the error.

Edit_AddIW

Adds an inline structure.

Type: Subroutine   **Category**: Edit

Notes: The Edit_IW subroutine must be included in the code after Edit_AddIW, and must call the newly added inline structure in order for it to be saved to the geometry file. Edit_IW brings up the Inline Structure Editor. No edits are necessary to save the new inline structure, the editor has to just open and close. Without Edit_IW, once the code has been completed and the HECRASController closes, HEC-RAS will close and the newly added inline structure will be lost.

Arguments: **river** (string). The river name to add the inline structure to.

reach (string). The reach name to add the inline structure to.

rs (string). The river station of the new inline structure.

errmsg (string). If an error occurs within the RAS Controller, RC Returns a string containing a description of the error.

Edit_AddLW

Adds a lateral structure.

Type: Subroutine   **Category**: Edit

Notes: The Edit_LW subroutine must be included in the code after Edit_AddLW, and must call the newly added lateral structure in order for it to be saved to the geometry file. Edit_LW brings up the Lateral Structure Editor. No edits are necessary to save the new lateral structure, the editor has to just open and close. Without Edit_LW, once the code has been completed and the HECRASController closes, HEC-RAS will close and the newly added lateral structure will be lost.

Arguments: **river** (string). The river name to add the lateral structure to.

reach (string). The reach name to add the lateral structure to.

rs (string). The river station of the new lateral structure.

errmsg (string). If an error occurs within the RAS Controller, RC Returns a string containing a description of the error.

Edit_AddXS

Adds a cross section.

Type: Subroutine   **Category**: Edit

Notes: The Edit_XS subroutine must be included in the code after Edit_AddXS, and must call the newly added cross section in order for it to be saved to the geometry file. Edit_XS brings up the cross section editor. No edits are necessary to save the new cross section, the editor has to just open and close. Without Edit_XS, once the code has been completed and the HECRASController closes, HEC-RAS will close and the newly added cross section will be lost.

Arguments: **river** (string). The river name to add the cross section to.

reach (string). The reach name to add the cross section to.

rs (string). The river station of the new cross section.

errmsg (string). If an error occurs within the RAS Controller, RC Returns a string containing a description of the error.

Edit_BC

Opens the Bridge/Culvert Editor and displays the selected river station.

Type: Subroutine   **Category**: Edit

Notes: Run-time is paused while edits are made in the Bridge/Culvert Editor. Once the Bridge/Culvert Editor is closed, run-time resumes.

Arguments: **river** (string). The river name of the bridge/culvert to edit.

reach (string). The reach name of the bridge/culvert to edit.

rs (string). The river station of the bridge/culvert to edit.

Edit_GeometricData

Opens the Geometry Data window.

Type: Subroutine   **Category**: Edit

Notes: Run-time is paused while edits are made in the Geometry Data window. Once the Geometry Data window is closed, run-time resumes.

Arguments: None

Edit_IW

Opens the Inline Structure Editor and displays the selected river station.

Type: Subroutine   **Category**: Edit

Notes: Run-time is paused while edits are made in the Inline Structure Editor. Once the Inline Structure Editor is closed, run-time resumes.

Arguments: **river** (string). The river name of the inline structure to edit.

reach (string). The reach name of the inline structure to edit.

rs (string). The river station of the inline structure to edit.

Edit_LW

Opens the Lateral Structure Editor and displays the selected river station.

Type: Subroutine   **Category**: Edit

Notes: Run-time is paused while edits are made in the lateral structure editor. Once the Lateral Structure Editor is closed, run-time resumes.

Arguments: **river** (string). The river name of the lateral structure to edit.

reach (string). The reach name of the lateral structure to edit.

rs (string). The river station of the lateral structure to edit.

Edit_MultipleRun

Opens the Run Multiple Plans Dialog.

Type: Subroutine   **Category**: Edit

Notes: Run-time does not pause while the Run Multiple Plans Dialog is open, so it is suggested that a message box be added after Edit_MultipleRun, so that the subroutine does not end and close the dialog before the user can check plans.

Arguments: None.

Edit_PlanData

Opens the Steady or Unsteady Flow Analysis window for edits (whichever is current).

Type: Subroutine   **Category**: Edit

Notes: Run-time does not pause while the Flow Analysis Window is open, so it is suggested that a messagebox be added after Edit_PlanData, so that the subroutine does not end and close the window before the user can make edits.

Arguments: None.

Edit_QuasiUnsteadyFlowData

Opens the Quasi-unsteady Flow Editor.

Type: Subroutine   **Category**: Edit

Notes: Run-time does not pause while the Quasi-Unsteady Flow Editor is open, so it is suggested that a messagebox be added after Edit_QuasiUnsteadyFlowData, so that the subroutine does not end and close the window before the user can make edits.

Arguments: None.

Edit_SedimentData

Opens the Sediment Data Editor.

Type: Subroutine   **Category**: Edit

Notes: Run-time does not pause while the Sediment Data Editor is open, so it is suggested that a message box be added after Edit_SedimentData, so that the subroutine does not end and close the window before the user can make edits.

Arguments: None.

Edit_SteadyFlowData

Opens the Steady Flow Editor.

Type: Subroutine   **Category**: Edit

Notes: Run-time does not pause while the Steady Flow Editor is open, so it is suggested that a message box be added after Edit_SteadyFlowData, so that the subroutine does not end and close the window before the user can make edits.

Arguments: None.

Edit_UnsteadyFlowData

Opens the Unsteady Flow Editor.

Type: Subroutine   **Category**: Edit

Notes: Run-time does not pause while the Unsteady Flow Editor is open, so it is suggested that a message box be added after Edit_UnsteadyFlowData, so that the subroutine does not end and close the window before the user can make edits.

Arguments: None.

Edit_WaterQualityData

Opens the Water Quality Data Editor.

Type: Subroutine   **Category**: Edit

Notes: Run-time does not pause while the Water Quality Data Editor is open, so it is suggested that a message box be added after Edit_WaterQualityData, so that the subroutine does not end and close the window before the user can make edits.

Arguments: None.

Edit_XS

Opens the Cross Section Editor and displays the selected cross section.

Type: Subroutine   **Category**: Edit

Notes: Run-time is paused while edits are made in the Cross Section Editor. Once the Cross Section Editor is closed, run-time resumes.

Arguments: **river** (string). The river name of the cross section.

reach (string). The reach name of the cross section.

rs (string). The river station of the cross section.

ExportGIS

Exports HEC-RAS results to an *.sdf export file that can be read into GIS using HEC-GeoRAS.

Type: Subroutine   **Category**: Action

Notes: The Export GIS Editor does NOT open when this subroutine is called. HECRASController uses whatever user inputs (i.e. profiles to export, results to export, types of geometric data to export, etc.) have already been set in the Editor and only writes the *.sdf export file.

Arguments: None.

Geometry

Class of procedures specific to geometry.

Type: Class   **Category**: Class

Notes: See Geometry Class for specific procedures.

Arguments: None.

Geometry_BreachParamGetXML

Returns a string variable listing out the dam breach parameters of the current plan in XML format

Type: Function   **Category:** Info   **Returns:** String

Notes:

Arguments: None.

Geometry_BreachParamSetXML

Sets the dam breach parameters of the current plan using XML.

Type: Subroutine   **Category:** Action

Notes:

Arguments: **xmlText** (string).

Geometry_GetGateNames

Returns the number of gates and gate names for a specified inline structure.

Type: Subroutine   **Category:** Info

Notes:

Arguments: **river** (string). The river name of the inline structure.

reach (string). The reach name of the inline structure.

rs (string). The river station of the inline structure.

nGate (long, returned). The number of gate groups for the inline structure.

GateNames (string, returned). The array of gate group names for the inline structure.

> **errmsg** (string, returned). An error message returned by the HECRASController if there's a problem getting the gate names.

Geometry_GetGML

Returns the GML file text for the current geometry file.

Type: Function   **Category**: Info   **Returns**: String

Notes:

Arguments: **geomfilename** (string). The name of the geometry file.

Geometry_GetNode

Returns the node ID of a selected node.

Type: Function   **Category**: Info   **Returns**: Node ID (Long)

Notes: Node can be any geometric component with a River Station (i.e. cross section, bridge/culvert, inline structure, lateral structure, multiple opening).

Arguments: **riv** (string). The river name of the node.

                rch (string). The reach name of the node.

                rs (string). The river station of the node.

Geometry_GetNodes

Returns an array of nodes and node types in a specified river and reach.

Type: Subroutine   **Category**: Info

Notes: A node can be any geometric component with a River Station (i.e. cross section, bridge/culvert, inline structure, lateral structure, multiple opening).

Arguments: **riv** (long). The river ID.

                rch (long). The reach ID.

                nRS (long, returned). The number of nodes on the selected river/reach.

> **rs()** (string, returned). The array of River Stations representing nodes on the selected river/reach.
>
> **NodeType()** (string, returned). The array of node types on the selected river/reach.

Geometry_GetReaches

Returns an array of reach names in a specified river.

Type: Subroutine   **Category**: Info

Notes:

Arguments: **riv** (long). The river ID.

> **nReach** (long, returned). The number of reaches in the selected river.
>
> **reach()** (string, returned). The names of the reaches on the selected river.

Geometry_GetRivers

Returns an array of river names.

Type: Subroutine   **Category**: Info

Notes:

Arguments: **nRiver** (long, returned). The number of rivers.

> **river()** (string, returned). The names of the rivers.

Geometery_GISImport

*Imports geometry data from an *.sdf import file.*

Type: Subroutine   **Category**: Action

Notes: The Import Geometry Data from GIS Editor does NOT open when this subroutine is called. HECRASController uses default settings for importing. A new geometry file is created with this subroutine and all streams and nodes are imported. *Note the misspelling- "Geometery"- in the name of this subroutine.

Arguments: **title** (string). The title of the new geometry file to import.

Filename (string, returned). The path and filename of the sdf file.

Geometry_RatioMann

Changes Manning's n Values over a specified range of cross sections by the input ratio.

Type: Subroutine   **Category**: Action

Notes:

Arguments: **riv (long).** The River ID.

rchUp (long). The upstream reach ID in the range.

nUp (long). The upstream node ID in the range.

rchDn (long). The downstream reach ID in the range.

nDn (long). The downstream node ID in the range.

ratio (single). The ratio to apply to the Manning's n values in the range of cross sections.

errmsg (string, returned). An error message returned by the HECRASController if there's a problem changing the Manning's n values by ratio.

Geometry_SetMann

Sets the Manning's n Values, by stationing, for a cross section.

Type: Function   **Category**: Edit   **Returns**: True or False (Boolean)

Notes: If station values don't exist in the station elevation table, HECRASController will use the closest station to apply the n value to.

Arguments: **river** (string). The river to set Manning's n Values.

reach (string). The reach to set Manning's n Values.

rs (string). The river station of the cross section to set
Manning's n Values.

nMann (long). The number of Manning's n values to add.

Mann_n() (single). An array of the Manning's n values to add.

Station() (single). An array of the stationing values of the
Manning's n breakpoints.

errmsg (string, returned). An error message returned if
something goes wrong with setting Manning's n values.

Geometry_SetMannLChR

*Sets the Manning's n Values, by left overbank, main channel, and right
overbank, for a cross section.*

Type: Function   **Category**: Edit   **Returns**: True or False
(Boolean)

Notes:

Arguments: river (string). The river to set Manning's n Values.

reach (string). The reach to set Manning's n Values

rs (string). The river station of the cross section to set
Manning's n Values.

MannLOB (single). Manning's n Value for the Left Overbank.

MannChan (single). Manning's n Value for the Left Overbank.

MannROB (single). Manning's n Value for the Right Overbank.

errmsg (string, returned). An error message returned if
something goes wrong with setting Manning's n values.

Geometry_SetSAArea

Sets the Area of a Storage Area.

Type: Function   **Category**: Edit   **Returns**: True or False
(Boolean)

Notes: The Geometry_SetSAArea function works in runtime, sets the area, and
returns a "True" value. But, you must ShowRAS and then save the geometry.

Otherwise changes to SA area are not saved. Also, make sure to NOT close RAS during run time.

Arguments: **SAName** (string). The name of the Storage Area.

              Area (single). The area to set the Storage Area with.

              errmsg (string, returned). An error message returned if something goes wrong with setting the area.

GetDataLocations_Output

Gets all stage and flow hydrograph output locations, including their dss file names and dss paths.

Type: Subroutine   **Category**: Info

Notes:

Arguments: **PlanTitle** (string). The name of the Plan.

              DSSFiles() (string, returned). The array of DSS filenames.

              DSSPathnames() (string, returned). The array of DSS Pathnames.

              errmsg (string, returned). An error message returned if something goes wrong with getting output locations.

GetRASVersion

Returns the version number and date of HEC-RAS.

Type: Function   **Category**: Info   **Returns**: Version Number and Date (string)

Notes: Works the same as **HECRASVersion**

Arguments: **None.**

HECRASVersion

Returns the version number and date of HEC-RAS.

Type: Function   **Category**: Info   **Returns**: Version Number and Date (string)

Notes: Works the same as **GetRASVersion**

Arguments: **None.**

Map_Add

Adds a map to the Geometry Schematic.

Type: Subroutine   **Category**: Action

Notes: This adds a map, but does not turn it on.

Arguments: **Filename** (string). The path and filename of the image to add.

Output_ComputationLevel_Export

Exports the computation level output to a comma delimited text file. .

Type: Subroutine   **Category**: Output

Notes: For this to work, user must have a .hyd## file created, which contains the computation level output in binary form. The .hyd## file is created when the users runs HEC-RAS with the Computation Level Output box checked. Base level data sent to the text file is River, Reach, and River Station. Flow, Stage, Area, and Top Width are optional output parameters that can be sent. *Caution-this subroutine can take a long time to run and can create a very large text file.

Arguments: **filename** (string). The name to give to the new computation level text file.

errmsg (string, returned). An error message returned if something goes wrong with getting the count.

WriteFlow (boolean). True if you want flow data included in the computation level text file. Otherwise false.

WriteStage (boolean). True if you want stage data included in the computation level text file. Otherwise false.

WriteArea (boolean). True if you want area data included in the computation level text file. Otherwise false.

> **WriteTopWidth** (boolean). True if you want top width data included in the computation level text file. Otherwise false.

Output_GetNode

Returns the Node ID, for a given River Station.

Type: Function **Category**: Output **Returns**: Node ID (long)

Notes: Works like the Geometry_GetNode function, only this function reads from the output file, so an *.O## file is required (i.e. run computations first).

Arguments: **riv** (long). The river ID number.

rch (long). The reach ID number.

rs (string). The river station of the desired node ID.

Output_GetNodes

Gets an array of nodes and node types for a given river and reach.

Type: Subroutine **Category**: Output

Notes: Works like the Geometry_GetNodes subroutine, only this subroutine reads from the output file, so an *.O## file is required (i.e. run computations first). A node can be any geometric component with a River Station (i.e. cross section, bridge/culvert, inline structure, lateral structure, multiple opening).

Arguments: **riv** (long). The river ID.

rch (long). The reach ID.

nRS (long, returned). The number of nodes on the selected river/reach.

rs() (string, returned). The array of River Stations representing nodes on the selected river/reach.

NodeType() (string, returned). The array of node types on the selected river/reach.

Output_GetProfiles

Gets the profile names for the current plan.

Type: Subroutine   **Category**: Output

Notes: This function reads from the output file, so an *.O## file is required (i.e. run computations first).

Arguments: **nProfile** (long, returned). The river ID.

                     ProfileName() (string, returned). An array of profile names.

Output_GetReach

Returns the Reach ID for a given Reach name.

Type: Function   **Category**: Output   **Returns**: Reach ID (long)

Notes: This function reads from the output file, so an *.O## file is required (i.e. run computations first).

Arguments: **riv** (long). The river ID.

                     reach (string). The name of the reach.

Output_GetReaches

Gets an array of reaches for a given river.

Type: Subroutine   **Category**: Output

Notes: Works like the Geometry_GetReaches subroutine, only this function reads from the output file, so an *.O## file is required (i.e. run computations first).

Arguments: **riv** (long). The river ID.

                     nReach (long, returned). The number of reaches on the selected river.

                     reach() (string, returned). The array of reaches on the selected river.

Output_GetRiver

Returns the River ID for a given River name.

Type: Function   **Category**: Output   **Returns**: River ID (long)

Notes: This function reads from the output file, so an *.O## file is required (i.e. run computations first).

Arguments: **river** (string). The name of the river.

Output_GetRivers

Gets an array of rivers for the current HEC-RAS project.

Type: Subroutine   **Category**: Output

Notes: Works like the Geometry_GetReaches subroutine, only this function reads from the output file, so an *.O## file is required (i.e. run computations first).

Arguments: **nRiver** (long, returned). The number of rivers in the HEC-RAS project.

river() (string, returned). The array of rivers in the HEC-RAS project.

Output_NodeOutput

Returns an output value for a given node and profile.

Type: Function   **Category**: Output   **Returns**: Output Variable (Single)

Notes: The output value that is returned is for the HEC-RAS variable ID number, nVar. Variable numbers are defined in Appendix E.

Arguments: **riv** (long). The river ID number.

rch (long). The reach ID number.

n (long). The node ID number.

updn (long). 0 for upstream section, 1 for BR UP, 2 for BR DOWN. All other long integers return output for BR UP. Only applies to nodes that have an upstream and downstream section, like bridges, culverts, and multiple openings. For all other nodes, user can use any long integer number, makes no difference.

prof (long). The profile ID number.

nVar (long). The variable ID.

Output_ReachOutput

Gets an array of river stations, channel distances, and output values.

Type: Subroutine   **Category**: Output

Notes: The output values that are returned are for the HEC-RAS variable ID number, nVar. Variable numbers are defined in Appendix E. Caution: The rs() string array only returns cross sections, not other nodes like BR, IS, LS, etc. The **Output_NodeOutput** function's n (node id number) argument is based on a count of all of the river stations (including BR, IS, LS, etc.), so **Output_ReachOutput** and **Output_NodeOutput** are not compatible with each other. Another Caution: Output_ReachOutput returns an array of cross sections that are in reverse order of the typical convention of listing the most upstream cross section first. **Output_ReachOutput** assigns the downstream-most cross section index 1.

Arguments: **riv** (long). The river ID number.

rch (long). The reach ID number.

prof (long). The profile ID number.

nVar (long). The variable ID.

nRS (long, returned). The number of river stations in the reach.

rs() (string, returned). The array of river stations.

ChannelDist() (single, returned). The array of channel distances.

value() (single, returned). The array of values for the given variable ID.

Output_Variables

Gets an array of HEC-RAS output variable names and descriptions.

Type: Subroutine   **Category**: Output

Notes: The variable ID numbers are what are used for "**nVar**" in **Output_NodeOutput** and **Output_ReachOutput** procedures. The returned array index numbers correspond to the variable ID numbers. Variable numbers are defined in Appendix E.

Arguments: **nVar** (long, returned). The number of HEC-RAS variables (***not*** the variable ID!).

> **VarName()** (string, returned). The array of variable names.

> **VarDesc()** (string, returned). The array of variable descriptions.

Output_VelDist

Gets information about velocity distribution.

Type: Subroutine   **Category**: Output

Notes: Flow Distribution must be set as an option in the HEC-RAS model for any cross sections that will be called in this subroutine. If "Plot Velocity Distribution" is turned on then this subroutine will return data for all slices defined in the Flow Distribution Locations Editor. If "Plot Velocity Distribution" is turned off, this subroutine will return data for the left overbank, main channel, and right overbank.

Arguments: **riv** (long). The river ID number.

> **rch** (long). The reach ID number.

> **n** (long). The node ID number.

> **updn** (long). 0 for upstream section, 1 for BR UP, 2 for BR DOWN. All other long integers return output for BR UP. Only applies to nodes that have an upstream and downstream section, like bridges, culverts, and multiple openings. For all other nodes, user can use any long integer number, makes no difference.

> **prof** (long). The profile ID.

> **nv** (long, returned). The number of vertical slices.

> **LeftSta()** (single, returned). The array of left station values for each slice.

> **RightSta()** (single, returned). The array of right station values for each slice.

ConvPerc() (single, returned). The array of percent of total conveyance for each slice.

Area() (single, returned). The array of flow area values for each slice.

WP() (single, returned). The array of wetted perimeter values for each slice.

Flow() (single, returned). The array of flow values for each slice.

HydrDepth() (single, returned). The array of hydraulic depth values for each slice.

Velocity() (single, returned). The array of velocity values for each slice.

OutputDSS_GetStageFlow

Returns stage and flow for every hydrograph output interval.

Type: Function   **Category**: Output   **Returns**: True or False (Boolean)

Notes: An output file is not needed, since this function reads the DSS file. Therefore, postprocessing is not required, which could save a lot of time, if run time efficiency is required. DateTimeValue is in Julien format, returned as a double precision number, so either use the CDate() function to convert it to a date, or if sending to a worksheet, set the cell(s) formatting to date/time.

Arguments: **riv** (string). The river name.

rch (string). The reach name.

rs (string). The river station.

nvalue (long, returned). The number of hydrograph outputs.

ValueDateTime() (double, returned). The array of date/times in Julien format.

Stage() (single, returned). The array of stage values.

Flow() (single, returned). The array of flow values.

errmsg (string, returned). An error message returned if something goes wrong with getting output.

OutputDSS_GetStageFlowSA

Returns stage and flow for every hydrograph output interval for a storage area.

Type: Function   **Category**: Output   **Returns**: True or False (Boolean)

Notes: An output file is not needed, since this function reads the DSS file. Therefore, postprocessing is not required, which could save a lot of time, if run time efficiency is required. DateTimeValue is in Julien format, returned as a double precision number, so either use the CDate() function to convert it to a date, or if sending to a worksheet, set the cell(s) formatting to date/time. Names for storage areas cannot be read using the HECRASController, therefore the storage area name has to be hard coded, read from an Excel® worksheet, or retrieved interactively during run-time.

Arguments: **StorageArea** (string). The storage area name.

    nvalue (long, returned). The number of hydrograph outputs.

    ValueDateTime() (double, returned). The array of date/times in Julien format.

    Stage() (single, returned). The array of stage values.

    Flow() (single, returned). The array of flow values.

    errmsg (string, returned). An error message returned if something goes wrong with getting output.

Plan_GetFilename

Given a plan name, returns the plan file, including path.

Type: Function   **Category**: Info   **Returns**: Plan file and path (String)

Notes:

Arguments: **planName** (string). The name of the plan.

Plan_GetParameterUncertaintyXML

Not available. Will be for Monte Carlo Analysis in future version of HEC-RAS.

Type: Function   **Category**: Info   **Returns**: String

Notes:

Arguments: **None**

Plan_InformationXML

Not available. Will be for Monte Carlo Analysis in future version of HEC-RAS.

Type: Function   **Category:** Info   **Returns:** String

Notes:

Arguments: **None**

Plan_Names

Gets an array of all of the Plan Names in the active HEC-RAS project.

Type: Subroutine   **Category:** Info

Notes:

Arguments: **PlanCount** (long, returned). The number of plans.

PlanNames() (string, returned). The array of plan names.

IncludeOnlyPlansInBaseDirectory (boolean).

Plan_Reports

Lists out the output plan "reports"

Type: Subroutine   **Category:** Info

Notes: Plan Reports are the "Cross Section Plot", "Profile Plot", "XYZ Plot", "Cross Section Table", and "Profile Table". Does not print out the reports, only lists the names of the available reports.

Arguments: **ReportCount** (long, returned). The number of plan reports.

ReportNames() (string, returned). The array of plan reports.

Plan_SetCurrent

Changes the current plan in the HEC-RAS project to the supplied Plan Name.

Type: Function   **Category**: Action   **Returns**: True or False (Boolean)

Notes:

Arguments: **PlanTitleToSet** (string). The name of the plan to set.

Plan_SetParameterUncertaintyXML

Not available. Will be for Monte Carlo Analysis in future version of HEC-RAS.

Type: Subroutine   **Category**: Action

Notes:

Arguments: **xmlText** (string)

PlanOutput_IsCurrent

Checks to see if a plan has an output file associated with it.

Type: Function   **Category**: Action   **Returns**: True or False (Boolean)

Notes: Displays a RAS window that shows a list of all of the current plans in the RAS Project, and indicates the name and index number of the plan to check if it has been computed. If it does not have an output file (i.e. hasn't been computed), a message box will ask if you want to run the plan. A message box pops up that requires the user to click OK to continue with run-time. Otherwise the RAS "Current Plan" window opens and closes quickly.

Arguments: **PlanTitleToCheck** (string). The name of the plan to check.

ShowMessageList (boolean). Whether or not to display a message box showing the plans.

errmsg (string, returned). An error message returned if something goes wrong with this function.

PlanOutput_SetCurrent

Sets the plan output to the selected plan.

Type: Function   **Category**: Action   **Returns**: True or False (Boolean)

Notes: This only works if an output file exists for the selected plan. Does not change the current plan, only changes the output file that is displayed in the output tables and plots.

Arguments: **PlanTitleToSet** (string). The plan title whose output to set as active.

PlanOutput_SetMultiple

Sets which plans to set to view in output plots and tables.

Type: Function   **Category**: Action   **Returns**: Number of plans set (Long)

Notes: Sets the multiple plan outputs. Only works if output files exist for the selected plan. *Note, does not change the current plan, only changes the output files that are displayed in the output tables and plots. **Note, PlanOutput_SetMultiple requires a 0-based array for Plan_TitleToSet_0. The subroutine Plan_Names returns a 1-based array so it must be converted to 0-based, prior to calling PlanOutput_SetMultiple.

Arguments: **nPlanTitleToSet** (long)

PlanTitleToSet_0() (string). 0-based array of plan titles to set.

ShowMessageList (boolean). Whether to have RAS display a message box showing the plan names.

PlotHydraulicTables

Displays the Hydraulic Property Plot for a given River, Reach, and River Station.

Type: Subroutine   **Category**: Plot

Notes: For unsteady flow plans only.

Arguments: **river** (string). The river name.

reach (string). The reach name.

rs (string). The river station.

PlotPF

Displays the Water Surface Profile Plot for a given River and Reach.

Type: Subroutine   **Category**: Plot

Notes: Must have an output file for this to work.

Arguments: **river** (string). The river name.

reach (string). The reach name.

PlotPFGeneral

Displays the General Profile Plot for a given River and Reach.

Type: Subroutine   **Category**: Plot

Notes: Must have an output file for this to work.

Arguments: **river** (string). The river name.

reach (string). The reach name.

PlotRatingCurve

Displays the Rating Curve for a given River, Reach, and River Station.

Type: Subroutine   **Category**: Plot

Notes: Must have an output file for this to work.

Arguments: **river** (string). The river name.

reach (string). The reach name.

rs (string). The river station.

PlotStageFlow

Displays the Stage and Flow Hydrograph for a given River, Reach, and River Station.

Type: Subroutine   **Category**: Plot

Notes: For unsteady flow plans only. Must have an output file for this to work.

Arguments: **river** (string). The river name.

                        reach (string). The reach name.

                        rs (string). The river station.

PlotStageFlowSA

Displays the Stage and Flow Hydrograph for a given Storage Area.

Type: Subroutine   **Category**: Plot

Notes: For unsteady flow plans only. Must have an output file for this to work. Names for storage areas cannot be read using the HECRASController, therefore the storage area name has to be hard coded, read from an Excel® worksheet, or retrieved interactively during run-time.

Arguments: **SAName** (string). The storage area name.

PlotXS

Displays the Cross Section Plot for a given River, Reach, and River Station.

Type: Subroutine   **Category**: Plot

Notes:

Arguments: **river** (string). The river name.

                        reach (string). The reach name.

                        rs (string). The river station.

PlotXYZ

Displays the XYZ Plot for a given River and Reach.

Type: Subroutine   **Category**: Plot

Notes:

Arguments: **river** (string). The river name.

reach (string). The reach name.

Project_Current

Returns the file name and path of the current HEC-RAS project.

Type: Function   **Category**: Info   **Returns**: File name and Path (String)

Notes:

Arguments: **None.**

Project_New

Starts a new HEC-RAS project with a given project file name and path and sets the title.

Type: Subroutine   **Category**: Action

Notes:

Arguments: **title** (string). The title of the new HEC-RAS project.

Filename (string). The path and file name of the new HEC-RAS project.

Project_Open

Opens an HEC-RAS project with a given project file name and path.

Type: Subroutine   **Category**: Action

Notes:

Arguments: **ProjectFileName** (string). Path and file name of the HEC-RAS project to open.

Project_Save

Saves the current HEC-RAS project.

Type: Subroutine   **Category**: Action

Notes:

Arguments: **None.**

Project_SaveAs

Saves a new project with a given project file name and path.

Type: Subroutine   **Category**: Action

Notes:

Arguments: **newProjectName** (string). Path and file name of the HEC-RAS project to save as.

QuitRAS

Closes HEC-RAS.

Type: Subroutine   **Category**: Action

Notes: QuitRAS should be called at the end of each procedure that opens an HEC-RAS project. Without QuitRAS, RAS will remain open as a process after the procedure is completed.

Arguments: **None.**

Schematic_ReachCount

Returns the number of reaches in the current HEC-RAS project's active geometry.

Type: Function   **Category**: Info   **Returns**: Number of Reaches (Long)

Notes:

Arguments: **None.**

Schematic_ReachPointCount

Returns the total number or reach vertex points that make up all of the schematic reach lines in the active geometry.

Type: Function   **Category**: Info   **Returns**: Number of reach
vertex points (Long)

Notes:

Arguments: None.

Schematic_ReachPoints

Returns arrays of rivers, reaches, and x-y coordinates for each reach.

Type: Subroutine   **Category**: Info

Notes: All array parameters are 0-based for this subroutine and must be redimensioned to (ReachCount-1) or (ReachPointCount-1)

Arguments: **RiverName_0()** (string, returned). The array of river names.

ReachName_0() (string, returned). The array of reach names.

ReachStartIndex_0() (long, returned). The array of starting index numbers for coordinate points.

ReachPointCount_0() (long, returned). The array of the number of reach points for each reach.

ReachPointX_0() (double, returned). The array of reach x coordinate points.

ReachPointY_0() (double, returned). The array of reach y coordinate points.

Schematic_XSCount

Returns the number of cross sections in the current HEC-RAS project's active geometry.

Type: Function   **Category**: Info   **Returns**: Number of Cross
Sections (Long)

Notes:

Arguments: None.

Schematic_XSPointCount

Returns the total number or cross section vertex points that make up all of the cross sections in the active geometry.

Type: Function   **Category**: Info   **Returns**: Number of cross section points (Long)

Notes:

Arguments: **None.**

Schematic_XSPoints

Returns arrays of river stations, their reaches, and arrays of x-y coordinates for each river station.

Type: Subroutine   **Category**: Info

Notes: All array paameters are 0-based for this subroutine and must be redimensioned to (XSCount-1) or (XSPointCount-1)

Arguments: **RSName_0()** (string, returned). The array of river stations.

ReachIndex_0() (long, returned). The array of reach IDs.

XSStartIndex_0() (long, returned). The array of starting index numbers for coordinate points.

XSPointCount_0() (long, returned). The array of the number of cross section points for each cross section.

XSPointX_0() (double, returned). The array of cross section x coordinate points.

XSPointY_0() (double, returned). The array of cross section y coordinate points.

ShowRAS

Displays the main HEC-RAS window.

Type: Subroutine   **Category**: Action

Notes: Once a RAS project has been open, ShowRAS will display it. Just opening a RAS project, only opens it as a process running in the background. You have to ShowRAS to see it on your monitor. Run-time must be paused in some way to be able to see HEC-RAS though. If the RAS Controller is defined within a subroutine, as soon as that subroutine has been executed and completed, the instance of HECRASController will close (thus closing the HEC-RAS application). To keep HEC-RAS open throw out a message box that requires user interaction to close, which effectively pauses the run-time.

Arguments: **None.**

SteadyFlow_ClearFlowData

Clears the flow data in the current plan's steady flow file.

Type: Subroutine   **Category**: Action

Notes: For steady flow plans only.

Arguments: **None.**

SteadyFlow_FixedWSBoundary

Sets fixed water surface boundary conditions.

Type: Function   **Category**: Edit   **Returns**: True or False (Boolean)

Notes: For steady flow plans only. The WSElev() array contains fixed water surface elevations for each profile in the active plan's flow file.

Arguments: **river** (string). The River name.

reach (string). The Reach name.

Downstream (boolean). True if this is a downstream boundary. Otherwise False.

WSElev() (single). The array of water surface elevations to set as fixed water surface boundary conditions.

SteadyFlow_nProfile

Returns the number of steady flow profiles in the current plan's active steady flow file.

Type: Function   **Category**: Info   **Returns**: Number of profiles (Long)

Notes: For steady flow plans only.

Arguments: **None.**

SteadyFlow_SetFlow

For a given River Station, sets the flows for each profile in the active plan's steady flow file.

Type: Subroutine   **Category**: Edit

Notes: For steady flow plans only. If the River Station currently is not in the flow table, it will be added. Need to first determine the number of profiles to set up the item count in the Flow() array.

Arguments: **river** (string). The river name.

       reach (string). The reach name.

       rs (string). The river station.

       Flow() (single). The array of flow values to add.

TablePF

Displays the Profile Output Table for a given river and reach.

Type: Subroutine   **Category**: Tabulate

Notes:

Arguments: **river** (string). The river name.

       reach (string). The reach name.

TableXS

Displays the Cross Section Output Table for a given river, reach, and river station.

Type: Subroutine   **Category**: Tabulate

Notes:

Arguments: **river** (string). The river name.

reach (string). The reach name.

rs (string). The river station.

UnsteadyFlow_SetGateOpening_Constant

Sets the gate opening for a specified gate group to a constant value in the Time Series Gate Opening boundary condition.

Type: Subroutine   **Category**: Edit

Notes: The time interval in the TS Gate Opening boundary condition is set to 1 year.

Arguments: **river** (string). The river name.

reach (string). The reach name.

rs (string). The river station.

GateName (string). The gate group name to set a new gate opening height.

OpenHeight (single). The gate opening height to set.

errmsg (string, returned). An error message returned if something goes wrong with this subroutine.

wcf_ComputePlan

This function only works with WAT, CAVI, and FRA. These three HEC applications use the HECRASController to communicate with HEC-RAS.

wcf_CreateNewPlan

This function only works with WAT, CAVI, and FRA. These three HEC applications use the HECRASController to communicate with HEC-RAS.

wcf_InputDataLocations_Get

This function only works with WAT, CAVI, and FRA. These three HEC applications use the HECRASController to communicate with HEC-RAS.

wcf_InputDataLocations_Set

This function only works with WAT, CAVI, and FRA. These three HEC applications use the HECRASController to communicate with HEC-RAS.

wcf_OutputDataLocations

This function only works with WAT, CAVI, and FRA. These three HEC applications use the HECRASController to communicate with HEC-RAS.

wcf_SetOutputPlans

This function only works with WAT, CAVI, and FRA. These three HEC applications use the HECRASController to communicate with HEC-RAS.

Geometry Class

nNode

Returns the number of nodes in a reach.

Type: Function   **Category**: Info   **Returns**: Number of nodes (Long)

Notes:

Arguments: **riv** (long). The river ID.

rch (long). The reach ID.

NodeCType

Returns the crossing type of a given node.

Type: Function   **Category**: Info   **Returns**: Crossing Type (String)

Notes: Crossing Types: BR for Bridge, Culv for Culvert, IS for Inline Structure, LS for Lateral Structure, MO for Multiple Opening.

Arguments: **riv** (long). The river ID.

rch (long). The reach ID.

n (long). The node ID.

NodeCutLine_nPoints

Returns the number of coordinate points for a given cross section's cutline.

Type: Function   **Category**: Info   **Returns**: Number of points (Long)

Notes:

Arguments: **riv** (long). The river ID.

rch (long). The reach ID.

n (long). The node ID.

NodeCutLine_Points

Returns an array of cutline coordinate points.

Type: Subroutine   **Category**: Info

Notes:

Arguments: **riv** (long). The river ID.

rch (long). The reach ID.

n (long). The node ID.

PointX() (double, returned). The array of x coordinate points.

PointY() (double, returned). The array of y coordinate points.

NodeIndex

Returns the node ID for a given River Station.

Type: Function   **Category**: Info   **Returns**: node ID (Long)

Notes:

Arguments: **riv** (long). The river ID.

rch (long). The reach ID.

RS (string). The river station.

NodeRS

Returns the River Station of a node, given its node ID.

Type: Function   **Category**: Info   **Returns**: River Station (String)

Notes:

Arguments: **riv** (long). The river ID.

rch (long). The reach ID.

n (long). The node ID.

NodeType

Returns the node type, given its node ID.

Type: Function   **Category**: Info   **Returns**: Node Type (Long)

Notes: 1 = Cross Section, 2 = Culvert, 3 = Bridge, 4 = Multiple Opening, 5 = Inline Structure, 6 = Lateral Structure.

Arguments: **riv** (long). The river ID.

                        rch (long). The reach ID.

                        n (long). The node ID.

nReach

Returns the number of reaches for a given river ID.

Type: Function   **Category**: Info   **Returns**: Number of Reaches (Long)

Notes:

Arguments: **riv** (long). The river ID.

nRiver

Returns the number of rivers in the active geometry.

Type: Function   **Category**: Info   **Returns**: Number of Rivers (Long)

Notes:

Arguments: **None.**

ReachIndex

Returns the ID of a reach, given its name.

Type: Function   **Category**: Info   **Returns**: Reach ID (Long)

Notes:

Arguments: **riv** (long). The river ID.

ReachName (string). The reach name.

ReachInvert_nPoints

Returns the number of points that make up the stream centerline of a reach, given the river and reach IDs.

Type: Function   **Category**: Info   **Returns**: Number of points (Long)

Notes: 1 = Cross Section, 2 = Culvert, 3 = Bridge, 4 = Multiple Opening, 5 = Inline Structure, 6 = Lateral Structure.

Arguments: **riv** (long). The river ID.

                              rch (long). The reach ID.

ReachInvert_Points

Gets an array of coordinate points that make up a reach stream centerline.

Type: Subroutine   **Category**: Info

Notes:

Arguments: **riv** (long). The river ID.

                              rch (long). The reach ID.

                              pointX() (double, returned). The array of x coordinate points for the reach.

                              pointY() (double, returned). The array of y coordinate points for the reach.

ReachName

Returns the name of the reach, given a reach ID.

Type: Function   **Category**: Info   **Returns**: The Reach Name (String)

Notes:

Arguments: **riv** (long). The river ID.

rch (long). The reach ID.

RiverIndex

Returns the river ID, given its name.

Type: Function   **Category**: Info   **Returns**: The River ID (Long)

Notes:

Arguments: **RiverName** (string). The river name.

RiverName

Returns the name of the river, given a river ID.

Type: Function   **Category**: Info   **Returns**: The River Name (String)

Notes:

Arguments: **riv** (long). The river ID.

Save

Saves the geometry.

Type: Subroutine   **Category**: Action

Notes:

Arguments: **None.**

APPENDIX B. THE GEOMETRY INPUT FILE KEYS

Key	1	2	3	4	5	6	7	8	9	10	11	12
2D Cell Volume Filter Tolerance	Volume Filter Tolerance											
2D Flow Area Cell Volume filter tolerance												
2D Face Area Elevation Conveyance Ratio	Conveyance Ratio											
2D Flow Area Face Conveyance Tolerance Ratio												
2D Face Area Elevation Profile Filter Tolerance	Area Elevation Profile Filter Tolerance											
2D Flow Area Face Area-Elevation Tolerance												
2D Face Profile Filter Tolerance	Face Profile Filter											

Key	1	2	3	4	5	6	7	8	9	10	11	12
	Tolerance											
2D Flow Area Face Profile Filter Tolerance												
		Number of Station Elevation Pairs for Upstream Sloping Abutment	Number of Station Elevation Pairs for Downstream Sloping Abutment									
Abutment Skew #Up #Dn	*blank*			*(Comma Delimited)*								
(Next Line after Abutment Skew #Up #Dn)	Upstream First Station	Upstream Second Station	*(continue for more…)*	*(Fields of 8)*								
(Next Line)	Upstream First Elevation	Upstream Second Elevation	*(continue for more…)*	*(Fields of 8)*								
(Next Line)	Downstream First Station	Downstream Second Station	*(continue for more…)*	*(Fields of 8)*								
(Next Line)	Downstream First Elevation	Downstream Second Elevation	*(continue for more…)*	*(Fields of 8)*								
Abutment Skew Station/Elevation Pairs												
Bank Sta	Left Bank Station	Right Bank Station										
Bank Stations for a cross section												

Key	1	2	3	4	5	6	7	8	9	10	11	12
BC Design	Elevation of High Chord (Top of Road)	Elevation of Low Chord	Add Vertical Walls in Deck? 0 for unchecked, 1 for checked	Opening Width	Add Sloping Abutments? 0 for unchecked, 1 for checked	Side Slope	Number of Piers	Upstream XS Starting Station	Downstream XS Starting Station	Pier Centerline Spacing	(Comma Delimited)	

Bridge Design Editor Inputs

Key	1
BC HTab FreeFlow Pts	Number of Htab Freeflow points

Number of HTAB Freeflow Points for a Bridge/Culvert. Only present in the text file if the default value is not used.

Key	1
BC HTab HWMax	Headwater Maximum Elevation

Bridge/Culvert HTAB Headwater Maximum Elevation

Key	1
BC HTab MaxFlow	Maximum Flow

Bridge/Culvert HTAB Maximum Flow. Only present in the text file if the default value is not used.

Key
BC HTab Sub Flow Curves

Number of HTAB Submerged Curves for a Bridge/Culvert. Only present in the text file if the default value is not used.

Key	1
BC HTab Sub Flow Pts	Number of Htab Points on each Submerged Curve

Number of HTAB Points on each Submerged Curve for a Bridge/Culvert. Only present in the text file if the default value is not used.

Key	1	2	3	4	5	6	7	8	9	10	11	12
BC Htab TWMax	Tailwater Maximum Elevation											
Bridge/Culvert HTAB Tailwater Maximum Elevation. Only present in the text file if the default value is not used.												
	X Coordinate of the End Point	Y Coordinate of the End Point	(Comma Delimited)									
BC Line End Position												
Ending position of a Boundary Condition Line												
	X Coordinate of the Middle Point	Y Coordinate of the Middle Point	(Comma Delimited)									
BC Line Middle Position												
Middle position of a Boundary Condition Line												
BC Line Name	Name of the 2D Boundary Condition Line											
Name of a 2D Flow Area External Boundary Condition Line												
	X Coordinate of the Start Point	Y Coordinate of the Start Point	(Comma Delimited)									
BC Line Start Position												
Starting position of a Boundary Condition Line												
BC Line Storage Area	Name of the 2D Area											
Name of the 2D Area the BC Line is connected to.												

186

Key	1	2	3	4	5	6	7	8	9	10	11	12
BC Line Text Position	X Coordinate of the upper point for the BC Line Name Label	Y Coordinate of the upper point for the BC Line Name Label	*(Comma Delimited)*									
BC Mult	Index for Multiple Opening Type. 1 for Conveyance, 2 for Culvert Group, 3 for Bridge	Upstream Stagnation Station Left	Upstream Stagnation Station Right	Downstream Stagnation Station Left	Downstream Stagnation Station Right	*(Comma Delimited)*						
Multiple Opening Parameters. Repeated for each multiple opening in a crossing.												
BC Use User Htab Curves	Use User Edited Curves in Computations? 0 for unchecked, -1 for checked											
User Defined HTab Curves												
BC User HTab FreeFlow(D)	Number of Flow/Elevation pairs for the User											

Key	1	2	3	4	5	6	7	8	9	10	11	12
	Defined Htab curves.											
					(Fields of 16. Two pairs per line. Continue with successive lines)							
(Successive Lines)	Flow	Elevation	Flow	Elevation								

User Defined HTab Curves

BEGIN DESCRIPTION	1	2	3	4	5	6	7	8	9	10	11	12
	The Description on for the node.	(continues on next lines for more text)										
(Successive Lines)												

Key to Indicate the next line(s) will be the node description.

	1	2	3	4	5	6	7	8	9	10	11	12
	Number of blocked obstructions for the current cross section	0 for Normal Blocked Obstructions, -1 for Multiple Blocked Obstructions										
#Blocked Obstruct (Next Line if Normal Blocked Obstructions)	Starting Stationing for a blocked area.	[leave blank]	Elevation of a blocked area.	Starting Stationing for a blocked area.	[leave blank]	Elevation of a blocked area. . .	(Fields of 8)						

Appendix B. The Geometry Input File Keys

Key	1	2	3	4	5	6	7	8	9	10	11	12
(Successive Lines if Multiple Blocked Obstructions)	Starting Stationing for a blocked area.	Ending Stationing for a blocked area.	Elevation of a blocked area.	Starting Stationing for a blocked area.	Ending Stationing for a blocked area.	Elevation of a blocked area. .	Starting Stationing for a blocked area.	Ending Stationing for a blocked area.	Elevation of a blocked area.	(Fields of 8)		

Blocked obstructions. The line(s) following the #Blocked Obstruct key depend on the type of blocked obstruction: normal or multiple.

Key	1	2	3	4	5	6	7	8	9	10	11	12
BR Coef	0 for Energy NOT checked, 1 for Energy checked for Low Flow	0 for Momentum NOT checked, -1 for Momentum checked	0 for Yarnell NOT checked, -1 for Yarnell checked	Pier Shape K	0 for WSPRO NOT checked, 1 for WSPRO checked	Blank	Submerged Inlet Cd	Submerged Inlet + Outlet Cd	High Flow Method: 0 for Pressure and/or Weir, -1 for Energy Only.	Coef Drag Cd	Low Flow Method to Use. 0 for "Highest Energy Answer", 1 for Energy, 6 for Momentum, 2 for Yarnell, 3 for WSPRO.	Max Low Chord

Bridge Modeling Approach Coefficients, Comma Delimited

Key	1	2	3
BR D Banks	Left Bank Station	Right Bank Station	(Comma Delimited)

Internal Downstream Bridge Cross Section Bank Stations (only included in the Geometry File if the default values have been changed).

Key	1	2	3	4	5	6	7	8	9	10	11	12
BR D #Mann	Number of Manning's n values											
(The line after)	First Manning's n Station	First Manning's n Value	Second Manning's n Station	Second Manning's n Value	Third Manning's n Station	Third Manning's n Value	Fourth Manning's n Station	Fourth Manning's n Value	Fifth Manning's n Station	Fifth Manning's n Value	(continues on successive lines for more points)	(Station/ n Value pairs in Fields of 8. 5 Pairs per line)

Key	1	2	3	4	5	6	7	8	9	10	11	12
Manning's n Values for Internal Downstream Bridge Cross Section												
BR D #Sta/Elev	Number of Station Elevation Pairs											
	Station of First Point	Elevation of First Point	Station of Second Point	Elevation of Second Point	Station of Third Point	Elevation of Third Point	Station of Fourth Point	Elevation of Fourth Point	Station of Fifth Point	Elevation of Fifth Point	(continues on successive lines for more points)	(Station Elevation Pairs in Fields of 8.5 Pairs per line)
(The line after)												
Internal Downstream Bridge Cross Section (only included in the Geometry file if the default values have been changed)												
BR U Banks	Left Bank Station	Right Bank Station	(Comma Delimited)									
Internal Upstream Bridge Cross Section Bank Stations (only included in the Geometry File if the default values have been changed).												
BR U #Mann	Number of Manning's n values											
	First Manning's n Station	First Manning's n Value	Second Manning's n Station	Second Manning's n Value	Third Manning's n Station	Third Manning's n Value	Fourth Manning's n Station	Fourth Manning's n Value	Fifth Manning's n Station	Fifth Manning's n Value	(continues on successive lines for more points)	(Station/n Value pairs in Fields of 8.5 Pairs per line)
(The line after)												
Manning's n Values for Internal Upstream Bridge Cross Section												
BR U #Sta/Elev	Number of Station Elevation Pairs											

Appendix B. The Geometry Input File Keys

Key	1	2	3	4	5	6	7	8	9	10	11	12
(The line after)	Station of First Point	Elevation of First Point	Station of Second Point	Elevation of Second Point	Station of Third Point	Elevation of Third Point	Station of Fourth Point	Elevation of Fourth Point	Station of Fifth Point	Elevation of Fifth Point	(continues on successive lines for more points)	(Station Elevation Pairs in Fields of 8. 5 Pairs per line)

Internal Upstream Bridge Cross Section (only included in the Geometry file if the default values have been changed)

Bridge Culvert	Momentum Equation Options. -1 for "Add friction component", 0 otherwise	Momentum Equation Options. -1 for "Add weight component", 0 otherwise	Pressure Flow Criteria. -1 for "Upstream energy grade line", 0 for "Upstream water surface"	Class B Defaults. -1 for "Inside the bridge at the upstream end", 0 for "Inside the bridge at the downstream end"	Ice Option. 0 for "No ice compute d...", 1 for "Ice remains constant ...", 2 for "Dynamic ice jam..."							

Computational Options for the Bridge. Note, this key uses a "_" instead of a "=" to separate key from input data.

Conn Culv Botton n	Manning's n for Culvert Bottom											

Storage Area Connection Culvert Manning's n Value for the bottom.

Conn Gate Name
WD,H,Inv,Gcoef,Exp_T,Exp_O,Exp_H,Type,Wcoef,Is_Ogee,SpillHt,DesHD,#Openings

Breaking the HEC-RAS Code

Key	1	2	3	4	5	6	7	8	9	10	11	12
(The line after)	Gate Group Name	Gate Width	Gate Height	Gate Invert	Sluice Discharge Coefficient	Radial Gate Trunnion Exponent	Radial Gate Opening Exponent	Radial Gate Head Exponent	Gate Type. 0 for Sluice, 1 for Radial, 2 for Overflow (Closed Top), 3 for Overflow (Open Top), 4 for User Defined Curves	Weir Coefficient	Type of Gate Sill Weir Shape. 0 for Broad Crested or Sharp Crested, -1 for Ogee crest.	Gated Spillway Approach Height
	13) Gated Spillway Design Energy Head	14) Number of Gates	15) Trunnion Height	16) Submerged Orifice Flow Orifice Coefficient	17) Head Reference. 0 for Sill, 1 for Center of Opening	18) Radial Gate Discharge Coefficient	19) Name of User Defined Curve Set	20) -1 if Sharp Crested Weir, 0 if otherwise	21) -1 for Rehbock Equation, 0 otherwise	22) -1 for Kindsvater-carter Equation, 0 otherwise	23) Index of L/b relationship. 0 for L/b = 1.0, 1 for L/b = 0.9, 2 for L/b = 0.8, etc.	
(continued)											(continues on next line for more stations)	
(The line after)	Centerline Station	Centerline Station	Centerline Station	Centerline Station	Centerline Station	Centerline Station	Centerline Station	Centerline Station	Centerline Station	Centerline Station		*(Comma Delimited)*
Conn HTab FreeFlow Pts	Htab Number of points on free											

Information about a given gate group. Nothing is listed on the key line. All general gate group values are placed on the next line (broken into two rows for display in this table. The line after that gets the centerline stations of the gates in this gate group. More than 10 centerline stations gets repeated on the next line. Each gate group gets its own key and successive lines of input data.

Key	1	2	3	4	5	6	7	8	9	10	11	12
	flow curve											
Storage Area Connection Culvert Htab points on the Free Flow Curve												
	Htab Head water maximu m											
Conn Htab HWMax	elevation											
Storage Area Connection Htab Headwater Maximum Elevation												
Conn HTab Sub Flow Curves	Htab Number of submerg ed curves											
Storage Area Connection Htab Submerged Curves												
	Htab Number of points on each submerg ed curve											
Conn HTab Sub Flow Pts	submerg ed curve											
Storage Area Connection Htab Number of points on each submerged curve												
	Htab Tail water maximu m											
Conn Htab TWMax	elevation											
Storage Area Connection Htab Tailwater Maximum Elevation												
	True if "Normal 2D Equation Domain", False if "Use											
Conn Overflow Method 2D												

Key	1	2	3	4	5	6	7	8	9	10	11	12
	Weir Equation "											
2D Overflow Computation Method												
	1 for Weir, 2 for Weir and Gates, 3 for Weir and Culverts, 4 for Linear Routing											
Conn Routing Type												
The Type of Storage Area Connection.												
	Linear Routing Coefficient in											
Conn Simple Spill Neg Coef	Negative Direction											
Storage Area Connection Linear Routing Coefficient in the Negative Direction. For Linear Routing only.												
	Linear Routing Coefficient in											
Conn Simple Spill Pos Coef	Positive Direction											
Storage Area Connection Linear Routing Coefficient in the Positive Direction. For Linear Routing only.												
	True for "Compute as Curves (faster), False for "Comput											
Conn Use RC Family												

Key	1	2	3	4	5	6	7	8	9	10	11	12
	e flow each time step"											
Compute as Curves, or Compute Flow each time step. Only applicable if the Connection Structure Type is 1, Weir.												
Conn Weir Coef			Weir Coefficient									
The Storage Area Connection Weir Discharge Coefficient												
Conn Weir Design EG	Design Energy Head											
The Storage Area Connection Weir's Design Energy Head. Used when the user selects to have HEC-RAS compute the weir coefficient. Only for Ogee Weirs.												
Conn Weir Design HT	Spillway Approach Height											
The Storage Area Connection Weir's Spillway Approach Height. Used when the user selects to have HEC-RAS compute the weir coefficient. Only for Ogee Weirs.												
Conn Weir Is Ogee	0 for Broad Crested, -1 for Ogee											
The type of Weir on the Storage Area Connection - Ogee or Broad Crested												
Conn Weir SE	Number of Station Elevation Pairs for the Weir Crest											
(The lines after Conn Weir SE Line)	Station of First Point	Elevation of First Point	Station of Second Point	Elevation of Second Point	Station of Third Point	Elevation of Third Point	Station of Fourth Point	Elevation of Fourth Point	Station of Fifth Point	Elevation of Fifth Point	(continues on successive lines	(Fields of 8)

Breaking the HEC-RAS Code

Key	1	2	3	4	5	6	7	8	9	10	11	12
											for more points)	

Storage Area Connection Station Elevation Points to define the top of the structure. The next line lists out the station and elevation points. Five pairs per line. More pairs can be added in additional lines.

Key	1	2	3	4	5	6	7	8	9	10	11	12
Conn Weir WD	Weir Width											

The Storage Area Connection Weir Width

Key	1	2	3	4
		X Coordinate of Upper Left of Storage Area Connection Text Box	Y Coordinate of Upper Left of Storage Area Connection Text Box	*(Comma Delimited)*
Connection	Name of Connection			

Key for a new storage area connection.

Key	1	2	3	4	5	6
	Number of Points that make up the Storage Area Connection Centerline					
Connection Centerline *(The lines after Connection Line)*	X Coordinate of First Point	Y Coordinate of First Point	X Coordinate of Second Point	Y Coordinate of Second Point	*(continues on successive lines for more points)*	*(Fields of 16)*

XY Coordinates of the Storage Area Connection Centerline. The following line includes XY pairs, with two pairs per line.

Key	1	2	3	4	5	6	7	8	9	10	11	12
Connection Culv	Culvert Shape. 1 for Circular, 2, for Box,...9 for Conspan Arch	Rise or Diameter	Span	Culvert Length	Manning's n for Top	Entrance Loss Coefficient	Exit Loss Coefficient	Chart #	Scale #	Upstream Invert Elevation	Downstream Invert Elevation	# Identical Barrels
(continued)	(13) Culvert ID	14) Solution Criteria. 0 for Highest U.S. EG, 1 for Inlet Control, 2 for Outlet Control.	(Comma Delimited)									
(The line after Connection Culv)	Upstream Centerline Station for first Barrel	Downstream Centerline Station for first Barrel	Upstream Centerline Station for second Barrel	Downstream Centerline Station for second Barrel	Upstream Centerline Station for third Barrel	Downstream Centerline Station for third Barrel	Upstream Centerline Station for fourth Barrel	Downstream Centerline Station for fourth Barrel	Upstream Centerline Station for fifth Barrel	Downstream Centerline Station for fifth Barrel	(continues on successive lines for more barrels)	(Fields of 8)

The Storgage Area Connection Culvert Parameters. The next line contains the upstream and downstream stationing for each culvert barrel.

Connection Desc	Storage Area Connection Description

Description of the Storage Area Connection

Key	1	2	3	4	5	6	7	8	9	10	11	12
	Name of the Downstream Storage Area											
Connection Dn SA												
The Name of the downstream Storage Area												
	Date (MMM/DDD/YYY) and Time (HH:MM:SS)											
Connection Last Edited Time												
The Date and time of the last edit of the Storage Area Connection												
	Number of Points that make up the Storage Area Connection Polyline											
Connection Line												
(The lines after Connection Line)	X Coordinate of First Point	Y Coordinate of First Point	X Coordinate of Second Point	Y Coordinate of Second Point	*(continues on successive lines for more points)*	*(Fields of 16)*						
XY Coordinates of the Storage Area Connection Polyline. The following line includes XY pairs, with two pairs per line.												
	Name of the upstream Storage Area											
Connection Up SA												

Key	1	2	3	4	5	6	7	8	9	10	11	12
The Name of the upstream Storage Area												
Culvert Bottom n	Manning's n for Bottom											
Manning's n value for the bottom of the culvert.												
Deck Dist Width WeirC Skew NumUp NumDn MinLoCord MaxHiCord MaxSubmerge Is_Ogee	Distance to U/S Cross Section	Deck Width	Bridge Deck Weir Coefficient	Deck Skew Angle	Number of Upstream Station/Chord Points	Number of Downstream Station/Chord Points	Min Weir Flow El	*blank*	Max Submergence	-1 for Ogee Crest, 0 for Broad Crested	U.S Embankment SS	D.S Embankment SS
(Next Line)	Spillway Approach Height (for Ogee Crests) 13)	Design Energy Head (for Ogee Crests) 14)	*(Comma Delimited)*									
(continued)	Upstream Cross Section Deck Station Point 1	Upstream Cross Section Deck Station Point 2	Upstream Cross Section Deck Station Point 3	*(continues for more points)*	*(Fields of 8)*							
(Next Line)	Upstream Cross Section High Chord Elevation Point 1	Upstream Cross Section High Chord Elevation Point 2	Upstream Cross Section High Chord Elevation Point 3	*(continues for more points)*	*(Fields of 8)*							
(Next Line)												

Key	1	2	3	4	5	6	7	8	9	10	11	12
	Upstream Cross Section Low Chord Elevation Point 1	Upstream Cross Section Low Chord Elevation Point 2	Upstream Cross Section Low Chord Elevation Point 3	(continues for more points)	(Fields of 8)							
(Next Line)	Downstream Cross Section Deck Station Point 1	Downstream Cross Section Deck Station Point 2	Downstream Cross Section Deck Station Point 3	(continues for more points)	(Fields of 8)							
(Next Line)	Downstream Cross Section High Chord Elevation Point 1	Downstream Cross Section High Chord Elevation Point 2	Downstream Cross Section High Chord Elevation Point 3	(continues for more points)	(Fields of 8)							
(Next Line)	Downstream Cross Section Low Chord Elevation Point 1	Downstream Cross Section Low Chord Elevation Point 2	Downstream Cross Section Low Chord Elevation Point 3	(continues for more points)	(Fields of 8)							
(Next Line)												

Characteristics of the Bridge/Culvert Deck. There is no input data on the same line as the key. The successive lines list out the input data for each bridge/culvert characteristic. The next line lists out the stations, upper chord elevations and lower chord elevations. All upstream stations are listed from left to right in the table. Followed by the U/S upper chord elevations, U/S lower chord elevations, D/S stations, D/S upper chord elevations, D/S lower chord elevation.

Dn River,Reach	River Name	Reach Name										

This key is repeated for every river/reach exiting the junction on the downstream side.

END DESCRIPTION

Key to indicate the end of the node description.

Key	1	2	3	4	5	6	7	8	9	10	11	12
Exp/Cntr	Expansion Coefficient	Contraction Coefficient	*(Comma Delimited)*									
Expansion and Contraction Coefficients												
	Folder and File of a geometry schematic background image	True if checked to display, otherwise false	Type of Raster (i.e. image, point, line, polygon)	CAD Suffix (i.e. [CADArea], [CADPoint], [CASLine]. Blank if not CAD file	Color ID number	*(Comma Delimited)*						
Geom Raster												
Background Image												
Geom Title	Geometry Title											
Title of the Geometry File.												
Ice Cohesion	Ice Cohesion											
Used if Ice Cover is entered for a cross section.												
Ice Fixed Mann	-1 if a Fixed Manning' s n Value is used, 0 if not.											
Used if Ice Cover is entered for a cross section.												
Ice Friction Angle	Internal friction angle of the Ice Jam (degrees)											

Breaking the HEC-RAS Code

Key	1	2	3	4	5	6	7	8	9	10	11	12
Used if Ice Cover is entered for a cross section.												
	-1 if Channel is selected for Wide River Ice Jams, 0 if not.											
Ice Is Channel												
Used if Ice Cover is entered for a cross section.												
	-1 if Overbanks are selected for Wide River Ice Jams, 0 otherwise.											
Ice Is OB												
Used if Ice Cover is entered for a cross section.												
	The K1 Coefficient											
Ice K1												
Used if Ice Cover is entered for a cross section.												
	Left Overbank Manning's n value of Ice	Channel Manning's n value of Ice	Right Overbank Manning's n value of Ice	*(Comma Delimited)*								
Ice Mann												
Used if Ice Cover is entered for a cross section.												
	The Maximum mean Velocity Under Ice Cover											
Ice Max Mean Vel												

Appendix B. The Geometry Input File Keys

Key	1	2	3	4	5	6	7	8	9	10	11	12
Used if Ice Cover is entered for a cross section.												
Ice Porosity	Ice Jam Porosity											
Used if Ice Cover is entered for a cross section.												
Ice Specific Gravity	Specific Gravity of Ice											
Used if Ice Cover is entered for a cross section.												
Ice Thickness	Left Overbank Thickness of Ice	Channel Thickness of Ice	Right Overbank Thickness of Ice	(Comma Delimited)								
Used if Ice Cover is entered for a cross section.												
#Inline Weir SE	Number of Station Elevation Points											
(The line after)	Station	Elevation	Station	Elevation	Station	Elevation	Station	Elevation	Station	Elevation	*(Fields of 8. Five pairs of Station Elevation values. Continue with successive lines)*	
Station Elevation Points for an Inline Structure												
IW **Dist,WD,Coef,Skew,MaxSub,Min_El,Is_Ogee, SpillHt,DesHD**	*(Nothing is listed after this key. All values are placed*											

203

Breaking the HEC-RAS Code

Key	1	2	3	4	5	6	7	8	9	10	11	12
	on the next line)											
(The line after)	Distance	Width	Weir Coefficient	Skew (not optional- always 0)	Maximum Submergence (not optional- always 0.95)	Minimum Elevation (not optional- blank)	0 for Broad Crested, -1 for Ogee	Spillway Approach Height	Design Energy Head	Upstream Embankment Side Slope	Downstream Embankment Side Slope	*(Comma Delimited)*

Inline Structure Input Data

Key	1	2	3	4	5	6	7	8	9	10	11	12
IW Gate Name WD,H,Inv,Gcoef,Exp_T ,Exp_O,Exp_H,Type, Wcoef,Is_Ogee,SpillHt, DesHD,#Openings	*(Nothing is listed after this key. All values are placed on the next line)*											
(The line after)	Gate Group Name	Gate Width	Gate Height	Gate Invert	Sluice Discharge Coefficient	Radial Gate Trunnion Exponent	Radial Gate Opening Exponent	Radial Gate Head Exponent	Gate Type. 0 for Sluice, 1 for Radial, 2 for Overflow (Closed Top), 3 for Overflow (Open Top), 4 for User Defined Curves	Weir Coefficient	Type of Gate Sill Weir Shape. 0 for Broad Crested or Sharp Crested, -1 for Ogee crest.	Gated Spillway Approach Height

Key	1	2	3	4	5	6	7	8	9	10	11	12
(continued…)	13) Gated Spillway Design Energy Head	14) Number of Gates	15) Trunnion Height	16) Submerged Orifice Flow Orifice Coefficient	17) Head Reference. 0 for Sill, 1 for Center of Opening	18) Radial Gate Discharge Coefficient	19) Name of User Defined Curve Set	20) -1 if Sharp Crested Weir, 0 if otherwise	21) -1 for Rehbock Equation, 0 otherwise	22) -1 for Kindsvater-carter Equation, 0 otherwise	23) Index of L/b relationship. 0 for L/b = 1.0, 1 for L/b = 0.9, 2 for L/b = 0.8, etc.	(Comma Delimited)
(Next Line)	Centerline Station	Centerline Station	Centerline Station	Centerline Station	Centerline Station	Centerline Station	Centerline Station	Centerline Station	Centerline Station	Centerline Station	(Fields of 8. Use Successive Lines for more than 10 Centerline Stations)	

Information about a given gate group. All general gate group values are placed on the next two lines. The line after that gets the centerline stations of the gates in this gate group. Each gate group gets it's own key and successive lines of input data.

IW Pilot Flow	Pilot Flow

Inline Structure Pilot Flow

Junc L&A	Junction Length	Junction Angle

Junction Length and Angle. This key is repeated for, and in the same order as every tributary entering or every distributary exiting the junction.

Junct Desc	1	2	3	4	5
	The Junction Description	Steady Flow Comp. Mode. 0 for Energy, -1 for Moment um	Moment um Eq. Friction Setting. 0 for no Friction, -1 for Add Friction	Moment um Eq. Weight Setting. 0 for no Weight, -1 for Add Weight	Unsteady Flow Comp. Mode. 0 for Force Equal WS Elevation s, -1 for Energy Balance Method

Key	1	2	3	4	5	6	7	8	9	10	11	12
The description of a junction and user selected computation modes. Comma Delimited.												
Junct X Y & Text X Y	The X Coord of the junction	The Y Coord of the junction	The X Coord of the Junction Name Label	The Y Coord of the Junction Name Label								
Junction coordinates and junction label coordinates. The coordinates for the label are defined at the upper left corner of the label feature.												
Junct Name	The Junction Name											
The name of a junction. This key starts a block of data related to the named junction.												
Lateral Weir Coef	Weir Coefficient (Cd)											
Lateral Structure Weir Coefficient												
Lateral Weir Connection Pos and Dist	0 for Left Overban k, 1 for Next to Left Bank Station, 2 for Next to Right Bank Station, 3 for Right Overban k	Tailwater Connecti on Distance to Upstrea m Cross Section.	*(Comma Delimite d)*									
Lateral Structure Tailwater Position												
Lateral Weir Distance	Headwat er Distance											
Headwater Distance to the Upstream Cross Section												

Key	1	2	3	4	5	6	7	8	9	10	11	12
Lateral Weir End	Tailwater River, blank if connected to Storage/2D Area or Out of System	Tailwater Reach, blank if connected to Storage/2D Area or Out of System	Tailwater River Station, blank if connected to Storage/2D Area or Out of System	Tailwater Storage Area or 2D Area, blank if connected to River Reach or Out of System	*(Comma Delimited)*							
Tailwater Connection												
Lateral Weir Flap Gates	0 for no Flap Gates, 1 for Flap Gates prevent Negative Flow, 2 for Flap Gates prevent Positive Flow											
Flap Gate Option for Lateral Structures												
Lateral Weir Hagers EQN	0 if not using Hagar's Equation, 1 if using Hagar's Equation	Default Weir Coefficient	Weir Average Height	Average Bed Slope	Weir Angle in Degrees	*(Comma Delimited)*						
Parameters for Hager's Equation. Values are comma delimited.												
Lateral Weir HW RS Station	Intersected River Station	Weir Station	*(continues on successiv*	*(Comma Delimited)*								

Key	1	2	3	4	5	6	7	8	9	10	11	12
			e lines for more stations)									

If User Specified Intersections are chosen for a lateral structure, the river station and corresponding Weir Station are entered here. This line is repeated for each User Specified Intersected River Station.

Key	1	2	3	4	5	6	7	8	9	10	11	12
	0 for Default Computed Intersections, 1 for User Specified Intersections											
Lateral Weir HW RS User Defined												

Lateral Structure Weir Stationing at HW XS's

Key	1	2	3	4	5	6	7	8	9	10	11	12
Lateral Weir Is Ogee	-1 for Ogee											

Ogee shaped crest for Lateral Structure. Only appears if Ogee is selected. Broad Crested is assumed by default

Key	1	2	3	4	5	6	7	8	9	10	11	12
Lateral Weir is Sharp	-1 for Sharp Crested											

Sharp Crested crest for Lateral Structure. Only appears if Sharp Crested is selected. Broad Crested is assumed by default.

Key	1	2	3	4	5	6	7	8	9	10	11	12
Lateral Weir is ZeroHeight	-1 for Zero Height Weir											

Zero Height crest for Lateral Structure. Only appears if Zero Height is selected. Broad Crested assumed by default.

Key	1	2	3	4	5	6	7	8	9	10	11	12
Lateral Weir Pos	0 for Left Overbank, 1 for Left Bank Station, 2 for Right Bank Station, 3 for Right											

Key	1	2	3	4	5	6	7	8	9	10	11	12
	Overban k											

Headwater position of the Lateral Structure

	1	2	3	4	5	6	7	8	9	10	11	12
Lateral Weir SE	Number of Station Elevation Points											
(The line after Lateral Weir SE)	Stationing of First Point	Elevation of First Point	Stationing of Second Point	Elevation of Second Point	Stationing of Third Point	Elevation of Third Point	Stationing of Fourth Point	Elevation of Fourth Point	Stationing of Fifth Point	Elevation of Fifth Point	*(continues on successive lines for more points)*	*(Fields of 8)*

Indicates the Start of a block of Station Elevation Points for the Node. The Station Elevation points are entered as x y pairs (stationing first, followed by elevation). There are 5 pairs of Station Elevation points per line.

	1	2	3	4	5	6	7	8	9	10	11	12
Lateral Weir SS	First Linear Routing Coef	Second Linear Routing Coef	Elevation of Spillway Crest	HW Distance to Upstream XS	*(Comma Delimited)*							

Lateral Structure Parameters for Linear Routing

	1	2	3	4	5	6	7	8	9	10	11	12
Lateral Weir TW Multiple XS	0 for a Point Between Two Cross Sections, -1 for Over Multiple											

Key	1	2	3	4	5	6	7	8	9	10	11	12
	Cross Sections											

Tailwater Flow into Cross Sections

	1	2	3	4	5	6	7	8	9	10	11	12
Lateral Weir TW RS Station	Tailwater River Station	Tailwater Connection Distance Downstream	*(continues on successive lines for more stations)*	*(Comma Delimited)*								

Lateral Structure tailwater River Station and Downstream Connection Distance

	1	2	3	4	5	6	7	8	9	10	11	12
Lateral Weir Type	0 for Weir/Gates/Culverts/Diversion Rating Curve	1 for Linear Routing	*(Comma Delimited)*									

Lateral Structure Type

	1	2	3	4	5	6	7	8	9	10	11	12
Lateral Weir WD	Weir Width											

Lateral Structure Weir Width

	1	2	3	4	5	6	7	8	9	10	11	12
Lateral Weir WSCriteria	0 for Energy Grade, -1 for Water Surface											

Lateral Structure Weir Flow Reference

	1	2	3	4	5	6	7	8	9	10	11	12
Levee	-1 for Left Levee, 0 for no Left Levee.	Station of Left Levee. Blank if no Left Levee.	Elevation of Left Levee. Blank if no Left Levee.	-1 for Right Levee, 0 for no Right Levee.	Station of Right Levee. Blank if no Right Levee.	Elevation of Right Levee. Blank if no Right Levee.						

Appendix B. The Geometry Input File Keys

Key	1	2	3	4	5	6	7	8	9	10	11	12
Levees. Can have a maximum of two levees, one on each side of the channel invert.												
LW Culv	Culvert Shape. 1 for Circular, 2, for Box,...9 for Conspan Arch	Rise or Diameter	Span	Culvert Length	Manning's n for Top	Entrance Loss Coefficient	Exit Loss Coefficient	Chart #	Scale #	Upstream Invert Elevation	Downstream Invert Elevation	# Identical Barrels
(Continued)	13) Culvert ID	14) Solution Criteria. 0 for Highest U.S. EG, 1 for Inlet Control, 2 for Outlet Control.	(Comma Delimited)									
(The line after LW Culv)	Upstream Centerline Station for first Barrel	Downstream Centerline Station for first Barrel	Upstream Centerline Station for second Barrel	Downstream Centerline Station for second Barrel	Upstream Centerline Station for third Barrel	Downstream Centerline Station for third Barrel	Upstream Centerline Station for fourth Barrel	Downstream Centerline Station for fourth Barrel	Upstream Centerline Station for fifth Barrel	Downstream Centerline Station for fifth Barrel	(continues on successive lines for more points)	(Fields of 8)
Lateral Structure Culvert Parameters. The next line includes the upstream and downstream centerline stations for the individual barrels in this culvert group type.												
LW Culv Bottom Depth	Depth to use	Bottom n										
The depth to use the bottom n value for this lateral structure.												
LW Culv Bottom n	Manning's n for Bottom											
Manning's n for Culvert Bottom for this lateral structure.												

Key	1	2	3	4	5	6	7	8	9	10	11	12
LW Culv Depth Blocked	Depth Blocked											
The depth blocked of the culvert for this lateral structure.												
LW Div RC	Number of Diversion Rating Curve Flow Pairs	False if Diversion based on water surface in channel, True if Diversion based on flow in the channel	Distance to Diversion	*(Comma Delimited)*								
(The line after LW Div RC)	Chan WS Elev or Chan Flow	Div Flow	Chan WS Elev or Chan Flow	Div Flow	Chan WS Elev or Chan Flow	Div Flow	Chan WS Elev or Chan Flow	Div Flow	Chan WS Elev or Chan Flow	Div Flow	*(continues on successive lines for more points)*	*(Fields of 8)*
Parameters for Diversion Rating Curve. The line after the key gets the diversion rating curve pairs.												
LW Gate Name WD,H,Inv,Gcoef,Exp_T,Exp_O,Exp_H,Type,W coef,Is_Ogee,SpillHt,D esHD,#Openings												
(The line after)	Gate Group Name	Gate Width	Gate Height	Gate Invert	Sluice Discharge Coefficient	Radial Gate Trunnion Exponent	Radial Gate Opening Exponent	Radial Gate Head Exponent	Gate Type. 0 for Sluice, 1 for Radial, 2 for Overflow (Closed Top), 3 for	Weir Coefficient	Type of Gate Sill Weir Shape. 0 for Broad Crested or Sharp Crested, -1 for Ogee crest.	Gated Spillway Approach Height

Appendix B. The Geometry Input File Keys

Key	1	2	3	4	5	6	7	8	9	10	11	12
									Overflow (Open Top), 4 for User Defined Curves			(Comma Delimited)
(Continued)	13) Gated Spillway Design Energy Head	14) Number of Gates	15) Trunnion Height	16) Submerged Orifice Flow Orifice Coefficient	17) Head Reference. 0 for Sill, 1 for Center of Opening	18) Radial Gate Discharge Coefficient	19) Name of User Defined Curve Set	20) -1 if Sharp Crested Weir, 0 if otherwise	21) -1 for Rehbock Equation, 0 otherwise	22) -1 for Kindsvater-carter Equation, 0 otherwise	23) Index of L/b relationship. 0 for L/b = 1.0, 1 for L/b = 0.9, 2 for L/b = 0.8, etc.	
(The line after)	Centerline Station	Centerline Station	Centerline Station	Centerline Station	Centerline Station	Centerline Station	Centerline Station	Centerline Station	Centerline Station	Centerline Station	(continues on successive lines for more points)	(Fields of 8)

Information about a given gate group. Nothing is listed on the lkey line. All general gate group values are placed on the next line (broken into two rows for display in this table. The line after that gets the centerline stations of the gates in this gate group. More than 10 centerline stations gets repeated on the next line. Each gate group gets its own key and successive lines of input data.

Key	1	2	3	4	5	6	7	8	9	10	11	12
#Mann	Number of Manning's n values	0 for Normal, -1 for Horizontal Variation	0 for Manning's n values, -1 for k values.	(Comma Delimited d)								
(The line after)	Starting Stationing for a new n value ("n value) Value	n Value	0		n Value	0	Starting Stationing for a new n value ("n value) Value	n Value	0			(Fields of 8)
(Successive Lines)	n Value Value		0		n Value	0		n Value	0			(Fields of 8)

213

Breaking the HEC-RAS Code

Key	1	2	3	4	5	6	7	8	9	10	11	12
	Breakpoint").			Breakpoint").			Breakpoint").					

Manning's n value settings. Second field is for the horizontal variation of Manning's n values. 0 for normal subsection breaks (i.e. Left overbank, main channel, right overbank) and -1 for horizontal variation in Manning's n Values.

	1	2	3	4	5	6	7	8	9	10	11	12
	Culvert Shape. 1 for Circular, 2, for Box,...,9 for Conspan Arch	Rise or Diameter	Span	Culvert Length	Manning's n for Top	Entrance Loss Coefficient	Exit Loss Coefficient	Chart #	Scale #	Upstream Invert Elevation	Downstream Invert Elevation	# Identical Barrels
(continued...)	13) Culvert ID	14) Solution Criteria. 0 for Highest U.S. EG, 1 for Inlet Control, 2 for Outlet Control.	15) Distance to Upstream Cross Section	*(Comma Delimited)*								
Multiple Barrel Culv	First Barrel Upstream Centerline Stationing	First Barrel Downstream Centerline Stationing	Second Barrel Upstream Centerline Stationing	Second Barrel Downstream Centerline Stationing	*(Fields of 8)*							
(Successive Lines)												

(Culvert Group Inputs)

Key	1	2	3	4	5	6	7	8	9	10	11	12
Node Last Edited Time	Date Time											
Date and time of the last time this node was edited. Date format (MMM/DD/YYY) and time format (HH:MM:SS)												
Node Name	The Node Name											
The name of the node, if one is given by the user.												
Permanent Ineff	F for non-permanent, T for permanent	(continues for each ineffective flow area)										
(Successive Line)	(Fields of 8)											
The line following this key will have either an F or T for each ineffective flow area (in order).												
Pier Skew	Pier Skew Angle											
The Skew Angle for the bridge piers.												
Pier Skew, UpSta & Num, DnSta & Num	blank	Centerline Station Upstream	Number of Pier Widths Upstream	Centerline Station Downstream	Number of Pier Widths Downstream	?	?	1 for "Apply floating debris...", 0 otherwise	Debris Width	Debris Height	(Comma Delimited)	
(Next Line after Pier Skew, UpSta & Num, DnSta & Num)	Upstream Pier Width	Upstream Pier Width	Continue for more...	(Fields of 8)								
(Next Line)	Upstream Pier Elevation	Upstream Pier Elevation	Continue for more...	(Fields of 8)								
(Next Line)	Downstream Pier Width	Downstream eam Pier Width	Continue for more...	(Fields of 8)								

215

Key	1	2	3	4	5	6	7	8	9	10	11	12
(Next Line)	Downstream Pier Elevation	Downstream Pier Elevation	Continue for more...	(Fields of 8)								

Repeated for each Pier. Multiple widths can be assigned to each pier, to define how the shape changes with elevation.

Key	1	2	3	4	5	6	7	8	9	10	11	12
Pump Station	Pump Station Name	X Coordinate of the Pump	Y Coordinate of the Pump	blank	blank	X Coordinate of the Pump Text	Y Coordinate of the Pump Text	(Comma Delimited)				

Key for the start of a new Pump Station.

Key	1	2	3	4	5	6	7	8	9	10	11	12
Pump Station From	River From	Reach From	River Station From	Storage Area From	Distance to the upstream RS to the pump intake	(Comma Delimited)						

The Location where it is pumping from. Can be a River Station or a Storage Area.

Key	1	2	3	4	5	6	7	8	9	10	11	12
Pump Station Group	Pump Station Group Name	True if "Bias group operations to On..." is selected, False otherwise.	Startup time in minutes	Shutdown n time in minutes	(Comma Delimited)							

Key for a New Pump Station Group.

Key	1	2	3	4	5	6	7	8	9	10	11	12
Pump Station Group HQ	Number of Head/Flo w pairs in the Pump											

Key	1	2	3	4	5	6	7	8	9	10	11	12
	Efficiency Curve											
(The line after Pump Station Group HQ)	Head for first point	Flow for first point	Head for second point	Flow for second point	Head for third point	Flow for third point	Head for fourth point	Flow for fourth point	Head for fifth point	Flow for fifth point	(continues on next line for more Head/Flow pairs)	(Fields of 8)

Pump Efficiency Curve. The next line includes head/flow pairs. 5 pairs per line. Additional pairs go in succeeding lined.)

Key	1	2	3	4	5	6
Pump Station Group Pump	Pump Name	WS Elev On	WS Elev Off	(Comma Delimited)		

This key presents information for a pump. Line is repeated for each pump in a group.

Key	1	2	3	4	5	6
Pump Station Reference	River	Reach	River Station	Storage Area	Distance to the upstream RS to the Reference	(Comma Delimited)

Optional On/Off Reference. Can be River Station or Storage Area

Key	1	2	3	4	5	6
Pump Station To	River To	Reach To	River Station To	Storage Area To	Distance to the upstream RS to the pump outlet	(Comma Delimited)

The Location where it is pumping to. Can be a River Station or a Storage Area.

Key	1
Pump Station TW Min	Highest elevation in pump line.

The Highest Elevation in the Pump Line.

Key	1
Program Version	Version

Breaking the HEC-RAS Code

Key	1	2	3	4	5	6	7	8	9	10	11	12
Version of HEC-RAS the Geometry File was last saved by.												
Rch Text X Y	x Coordinate	y Coordinate										
Coordinates of the Reach Name Text on the Geometry Schematic. Comma Delimited.												
	Number of vertices that make up this reach.											
Reach XY	x Coordinate of 1st Point	y Coordinate of 1st Point	x Coordinate of 2nd Point	y Coordinate of 2nd Point	(continues on next line for more points)	(Fields of 16)						
(Successive Lines)												
This key indicates the start of a table of xy coordinates of vertices that make up the reach schematic line. Each line following this key contains two pairs of xy coordinates.												
	0 for Normal, 1 for Reversed											
Reverse River Text												
Indicates whether the user has selected to reverse the direction of the River Name Text.												
River Reach	Name of River	Name of Reach										
Name of a river and reach. Each reach will have its own block of data starting with this key												
	Number of Station Elevation Pairs (500 max)											
#Sta/Elev	Stationing of First Point	Elevation of First Point	Stationing of	Elevation of	Stationing of Third Point	Elevation of Third Point	Stationing of	Elevation of Fourth Point	Stationing of Fifth Point	Elevation of Fifth Point	(continues on successive	(Fields of 8)
(Successive Lines)												

Key	1	2	3	4	5	6	7	8	9	10	11	12
			Second Point	Second Point			Fourth Point				e lines for more points)	

Indicates the Start of a block of Station Elevation Points for the Node. The Station Elevation points are entered as x y pairs (stationing first, followed by elevation). There are 5 pairs of Station Elevation points per line.

Key	1	2	3	4	5	6	7	8	9	10	11	12
Storage Area	Storage Area Name	X Coordinate of Upper Left of Storage Area Text Box	Y Coordinate of Upper Left of Storage Area Text Box	(Comma Delimited)								

Key for a new storage area.

Key	1	2	3	4	5	6	7	8	9	10	11	12
Storage Area 2D Points	Number of 2D Points											
(The lines after Storage Area 2D Points)	X Coordinate of Point 1	Y Coordinate of Point 1	X Coordinate of Point 2	Y Coordinate of Point 2	(continues on successive lines for more points-2 pairs per line)	(Fields of 16)						

Storage Area 2D Points Coordinates

Key	1	2	3	4	5	6	7	8	9	10	11	12
Storage Area 2D PointsPerimeterTime	Date formatted as DDMMMYYY	Time formatted as HH:MM:SS										

Unknown. Appears to always be set to 30Dec1899 00:00:00

Key	1	2	3	4	5	6	7	8	9	10	11	12
Storage Area Area	Storage Area Area											

Area of the Storage Area. Used only for Storage Area Type 0 and not a 2D Area...

219

Key	1	2	3	4	5	6	7	8	9	10	11	12
Storage Area Is2D	-1 for a 2D area, 0 for a regular storage area											
Whether this is a 2D area or a regular storage area.												
Storage Area Mannings	Manning' s n value											
Manning's n value for the 2D Area												
Storage Area Min Elev	Storage Area Min Elev.											
Minimum elevation of the Storage Area. Used only for Storage Area Type 0.												
	Upper Left Starting Point Offset X Coordinate (blank for default of 0)	Upper Left Starting Point Offset Y Coordinate (blank for default of 0)	Spacing DX	Spacing DY	*(Comma Delimited)*							
Storage Area Point Generation Data												
2D Flow Area Points Generation Data												
Storage Area Surface line	Number of Points that make up the Outline											
(The lines after Storage Area Surface Line)	X Coordina te of Point 1	Y Coordina te of Point 1	*(continue s on successiv e lines for more points)*		*(Fields of 16)*							

Key	1	2	3	4	5	6	7	8	9	10	11	12
The Outline of the Storage Area. The successive line includes the x and y coordinates of the vertex points that make up the storage area polygon. One vertex pair of coordinates per line.												
	0 for Area time Depth Method, 1 for Elevation versus Volume Curve											
Storage Area Type												
How is volume versus depth computed in HEC-RAS?												
Storage Area Vol Elev	Number of Elevation /Volume Pairs											
(The lines after Storage Area Vol Elev)	Elevation of First Point	Volume of First Point	Elevation of Second Point	Volume of Second Point	Elevation of Third Point	Volume of Third Point	Elevation of Fourth Point	Volume of Fourth Point	Elevation of Fifth Point	Volume of Fifth Point	(continues on successive lines for more points)	(Fields of 8)
Elevation/Volume Pairs for the Elevation versus Volume Curve												
Type RM Length L Ch R	Node Type ID.	River Mile of the Node.	Left Overbank Reach Length	Main Channel Reach Length	Right Overbank Reach Length							
Indicates the Start of a block of data for a node. The node type IDs are as follows: 1 for Cross Section, 2 for Culvert, 3 for Bridge, 4 for Multiple Opening, 5 for Inline Structure, 6 for Lateral Structure.												
Up River,Reach	River Name	Reach Name										
This key is repeated for every river/reach entering the junction from the upstream side.												

Key	1	2	3	4	5	6	7	8	9	10	11	12
Use User Specified Reach Order	0 for Do NOT use the User Specified Order for unsteady computations, -1 to use it.											
Use User Defined Reach Order for Computations?												
User Specified Reach Order	River	Reach										
User Defined Reach Order. This line repeats for all Reaches in the user defined order. Comma Delimited.												
Vertical n Elevations	Number of Elevations specified on the Vertical Variation Table											
	Elevation for first vertical variation point.	Elevation for second vertical variation point.	Elevation for third vertical variation point.	(continues for more points)	(Fields of 8)							
(Successive Lines)												
Used for Vertical Variation in n values												
Vertical n Flow	0 for n values by stage, 1 for n values by flow.											
Vertical variation in Manning's n values can be based on stage or flow.												

Key	1	2	3	4	5	6	7	8	9	10	11	12
Vertical n for Station	Starting Stationing for a new n value											
	Manning's n for first vertical variation point.	Manning's n for second vertical variation point.	Manning's n for second vertical variation point.	(continues for more points)	(Fields of 8)							
(Successive Lines)												

The stationing for each n value breakpoint. Each Starting Stationing gets its own Vertical n for Station line and successive n value line.

	1	2	3	4	5	6	7	8	9	10	11	12
Viewing Rectangle	x Coord of Left Edge	x Coord of Right Edge	y Coord of Top Edge	y Coord of Bottom Edge	(Comma Delimited)							

The coordinates of the geometry schematic view extents. Comma Delimited.

WSPro	1	2	3	4	5	6	7	8	9	10	11	12
	El of the top of the Left Embankment	El of the top of the Right Embankment	El of the toe of the Left Abutment	El of the toe of the Right Abutment	Abutment Type. 1, 2, 3, or 4.	Slope of the Abutments	Top Width of Embankment	Centroid stationing of projected bridge opening ...	Wing Wall Type. 0 for "No wing walls present", 1 for "Angular wing walls", 2 for Rounded wing walls	Length of Wing Wall	Angle of Wing Wall	Radius of entrance rounding
	13) Guide Bank Type. 0 for "No Guide Bank	14) Length of Guide Banks	15) Offset of Guide Banks	16) Skew of Guide Banks	17) "Piers are continuous", -1 for checked,	18) "Use Geometric Mean as Friction Slope method",	19) ?	20) C&E Losses "At approach Section", -1 for checked,	21) C&E Losses "At Guide Bank", -1 for checked,	22) C&E Losses "At upstream outside", -1 for	23) C&E Losses "At upstream inside (BU)", -1 for	24)C&E Losses downstream inside (BD)", -1
(continued...)												

Key	1	2	3	4	5	6	7	8	9	10	11	12
	Present", 1 for "Straight", 2 for "Elliptical"				0 for unchecked	-1 for checked, 0 for unchecked		0 for unchecked	0 for unchecked	checked, 0 for unchecked	checked, 0 for unchecked	for checked, 0 for unchecked
WSPRO Parameters, Comma Delimited												
XS Deck Add Priessmann Slot												
Used if the Priessmann Slot option was selected for the lid.												
	Number of xy Coords for the Cut Line											
XS GIS Cut Line	x Coordinate of 1st Point	y Coordinate of 1st Point	x Coordinate of 2nd Point	y Coordinate of 2nd Point	*(continues on next line for more points)*							
(Successive Lines)						*(Fields of 16)*						
Indicates the next series of lines will be xy coordinates of the Cut line for this node.												
XS Htab Horizontal Distribution	Number of Left Overbank Vertical Slices	Number of Main Channel Vertical Slices	Number of Right Overbank Vertical Slices	*(Comma Delimited)*								
Cross Section Htab Parameters - Vertical slices for velocity mapping.												
XS Htab Starting El and Incr	Htab Starting Elevation	Increment between Htab Computation Points	Number of Htab points	*(Comma Delimited)*								
Cross Section Htab Parameters												

Key	1	2	3	4	5	6	7	8	9	10	11	12
#XS Ineff	Number of Ineffective Areas	0 for Normal, -1 for Multiple (blocked)	(Comma Delimited)									
(Successive Line if Normal Ineffective Flow Areas)	Starting Stationing for an ineffective flow area.	[leave blank]	Elevation of an ineffective flow area.	Starting Stationing for an ineffective flow area.	[leave blank]	Elevation of an ineffective flow area.	(Fields of 8)					
(Successive Lines if Multiple Blocked Ineffective Flow Areas)	Starting Stationing for an ineffective flow area.	Ending Stationing for an ineffective flow area.	Elevation of an ineffective flow area.	Starting Stationing for an ineffective flow area.	Ending Stationing for an ineffective flow area.	Elevation of an ineffective flow area.	Starting Stationing for an ineffective flow area.	Ending Stationing for an ineffective flow area.	Elevation of an ineffective flow area.	(Fields of 8)		

Ineffective Flow Areas. The successive lines after this key are the station and elevations of the ineffective flow areas. The line(s) following the #XS Ineff key depend on the type of ineffective flow area: normal or multiple. If the ineffective flow area extends beyond the first cross section point, the value here should be set equal to the stationing of the first station elevation point of the cross section (normally "0").

Key	1	2	3	4	5	6	7	8	9	10	11	12
#XS Lid	Number of Lid Station Elevation Points											
(Successive Lines)	Stationing of First Lid Point	High Elevation of First Lid Point.	Low Elevation of First Lid Point.	Stationing of Second Lid Point	High Elevation of Second Lid Point	Low Elevation of Second Lid Point.	(continues on next line for more points)	(Fields of 8)				

Used if a Cross Section Lid has been entered.

Key	1	2	3	4	5	6	7	8	9	10	11	12
XS Rating Curve	Number of Rating Curve Points	0 for No Headwater Check, -1 for Headwater Check.	(Comma Delimited)									

Breaking the HEC-RAS Code

Key	1	2	3	4	5	6	7	8	9	10	11	12
(Successive Lines)	Discharge 1	Stage 1	Discharge 2	Stage 2	*(continues for more points)*	*(Fields of 8)*						

Used if a Rating Curve has been set for this cross section

APPENDIX C. THE STEADY FLOW INPUT FILE KEYS

Key	1	2	3	4	5	6	7	8	9	10	11	12
Boundary for River Rch & Prof#	This key is used for each reach, comma delimited	River Name	Reach name	Profile Number	(Comma Delimited)							
This key is used for each reach, to begin defining the boundary type(s). The Up and Down Boundary Requirements follow each one of these keys.												
Dn Known WS	Water Surface Elevation											
Downstream Boundary Known Water Surface Elevation												
Dn Rating Curve # Pts	Number of Stage/Discharge pairs that make up the Rating Curve											

Key	1	2	3	4	5	6	7	8	9	10	11	12
(The Line After Dn Rating Curve # Pts	First Discharge	First Stage	Second Discharge	Second Stage	Third Discharge	Third Stage	Fourth Discharge	Fourth Stage	Fifth Discharge	Fifth Stage	(Continues on next line for more Pairs)	(Fields of 8)

Downstream Rating Curve Boundary Condition. The next line(s) contain the rating curve as discharge/stage pairs. Five pairs per line.

Key	1	2	3	4	5	6	7	8	9	10	11	12
Dn Slope	Slope for Normal Depth Computation											

Downstream Boundary Slope for Normal Depth Computation

Key	1	2	3	4	5	6	7	8	9	10	11	12
Dn Type	0 for None, 1 for Known WS, 2 for Critical Depth, 3 for Normal Depth, 4 for Rating Curve											

Downstream Boundary Type for the Boundary Location and Profile listed above.

Key	1	2	3	4	5	6	7	8	9	10	11	12
DSS Import EndDate	Ending Date, DDMMM YYYY											

DSS Import Ending Date, for the Importing DSS Data Option

Appendix C. The Steady Flow Input File Keys

Key	1	2	3	4	5	6	7	8	9	10	11	12
DSS Import EndTime	End Time, HHMM											

DSS Import Ending Time, for the Importing DSS Data Option

Key	1	2	3	4	5	6	7	8	9	10	11	12
DSS Import FillOption	0 for No Interpolation, 1 for Linear Interpolation, 2 for Use Existing Flow Profiles as Ratios.											

DSS Import Interpolation method for missing DSS data

Key	1	2	3	4	5	6	7	8	9	10	11	12
DSS Import GetInterval	1 for "Select Profiles at the Following Intervals" checked. 0 if not checked.											

DSS Import Use Profile Interval, for the Importing DSS Data Option

Key	1	2	3	4	5	6	7	8	9	10	11	12
DSS Import GetPeak	1 for "Get Peak Flows at all Locations											

229

Key	1	2	3	4	5	6	7	8	9	10	11	12
	for Final Profile" checked. 0 if not checked.											
DSS Import Get Peak Flows option, for the Importing DSS Data Option												
DSS Import Interval	Interval for Selecting Profile											
DSS Import Profile Interval, for the Importing DSS Data Option												
DSS Import StartDate	Starting Date, DDMMM YYY											
DSS Import Starting Date, for the Importing DSS Data Option												
DSS Import StartTime	Start Time, HHMM											
DSS Import Starting Time, for the Importing DSS Data Option												
Flow Title	Title of the Flow File											
Title of the Flow File												
Gate Openings	River Name	Reach Name	River Station	Gate Name								

Appendix C. The Steady Flow Input File Keys

Key	1	2	3	4	5	6	7	8	9	10	11	12
(The Line After Gate Openings)	Gate Opening Height for First Profile	Number of Gates Open for First Profile	Gate Opening Height for Second Profile	Number of Gates Open for Second Profile	Gate Opening Height for Third Profile	Number of Gates Open for Third Profile	Gate Opening Height for Fourth Profile	Number of Gates Open for Fourth Profile	Gate Opening Height for Fifth Profile	Number of Gates Open for Fifth Profile	Continues on next line for more Pairs	(Fields of 8)

Steady Flow Gate Opening Boundary Condition Location. Following line(s) contain gate openings and number of gates open for each profile-five per line.

Key	1
Number of Profiles	Number of Flow Profiles

Number of Flow Profiles

Key	1	2	3	4	5	6	7	8
Observed WS	River Name	Reach Name	RS Name	Dn Distance	Observed WS Elevation for First Profile	Observed WS Elevation for Second Profile	(Continue for Observed WS Elevations for Remaining Profiles)	(Comma Delimited)

Location and information for Observed Water Surface Elevations. This key is repeated for each observed water surface elevation.

Key	1	2	3	4	5
Profile Names	First Profile Name	Second Profile Name	Third Profile Name	(Continues for more Profiles)	(Comma Delimited)

The Profile Names

Key	1
Program Version	HEC-RAS Version

Version of HEC-RAS the Steady Flow File was last saved by.

Key	1	2	3	4	5	6	7	8	9	10	11	12
River Rch & RM	River Name	Reach Name	River Station	(Comma Delimited)								
	Discharge values for Profiles at upstream boundary, Fields of 8											
(The Line After River Rch & RM)		First Profile Discharge	Second Profile Discharge	Third Profile Discharge	*(Continues for more Profiles)*	*(Fields of 8)*						
Location of an Upstream Boundary. The next line contains the discharge values at this location for each profile.												
Up Known WS	Water Surface Elevation											
Upstream Boundary Known Water Surface Elevation												
Up Rating Curve # Pts	Number of Stage/Discharge pairs that make up the Rating Curve											
(The Line After Up Rating Curve # Pts)	First Discharge	First Stage	Second Discharge	Second Stage	Third Discharge	Third Stage	Fourth Discharge	Fourth Stage	Fifth Discharge	Fifth Stage	*(Continues on next line for more Pairs)*	*(Fields of 8)*

Appendix C. The Steady Flow Input File Keys

Key	1	2	3	4	5	6	7	8	9	10	11	12

Upstream Rating Curve Boundary Condition. The next line(s) contain the rating curve as discharge/stage pairs. Five pairs per line.

| Up Slope | Slope for Normal Depth Computation | | | | | | | | | | | |

Upstream Boundary Slope for Normal Depth Computation

| Up Type | 0 for None, 1 for Known WS, 2 for Critical Depth, 3 for Normal Depth, 4 for Rating Curve | | | | | | | | | | | |

Upstream Boundary Type for the Boundary Location and Profile listed above.

APPENDIX D. THE UNSTEADY FLOW INPUT FILE KEYS

Key	1	2	3	4	5	6	7	8	9	10	11	12
Boundary Location	River Name (if boundary is River Station- Blank otherwise)	Reach Name (if boundary is River Station- Blank otherwise)	River Station (if boundary is River Station- Blank otherwise)	Downstream River Station (if boundary is uniform lateral inflow- Blank otherwise)	Storage Area Connection Name (if boundary is Storage Area Connection-Blank otherwise)	Storage Area Name (if boundary is Storage Area- Blank otherwise)	Pump Station Name (if boundary is Pump Station- Blank otherwise)	(blank)	(Comma Delimited)			
Boundary Condition Location. Starts a block of boundary condition information. Repeated for each boundary condition location.												
Critical Boundary Flow	The Max Change in Flow (without Changing Time Step)											

Key	1	2	3	4	5	6	7	8	9	10	11	12
The maximum change in flow without changing the time step.												
DSS File	DSS File name											
The file name of the dss file used for the boundary condition. Tied to the boundary condition location above.												
DSS Path	DSS Path											
The path for the boundary condition. Tied to the boundary condition location above.												
Elev Controlled Gate (Gate Group)		Upstream WS elevation at which gate begins to open	Upstream WS elevation at which gate begins to close	Gate Opening Rate	Gate Closing Rate	Maximum Gate Opening	Initial Gate Opening	ID for Reference Basis. 0 for Upstream WS, 1 for Specified Reference, 2 for Difference in Stage	*(Comma Delimited)*			
Input data for the elevation controlled gate boundary condition.												
Elev Controlled Gate Ref	Reference elevation at which gate begins to open	Reference elevation at which gate begins to close	First Reference e River. Blank if Storage Area used	First Reference e Reach. Blank if Storage Area used	Reference e River Station. Blank if Storage Area used	Reference e Storage Area. Blank if RS used	*(Comma Delimited)*					
Reference Location and opening/closing settings for gate control												
Elev Controlled Gate Stage Diff	Stage difference at which gate begins to open	Stage difference at which gate begins to close	First Reference e River. Blank if Storage Area used	First Reference e River. Station. Blank if Storage Area used	First Reference e Storage Area. Blank if RS used	Second Reference e River. Blank if Storage Area used	Second Reference e Reach. Blank if Storage Area used	Second Reference e River. Station. Blank if Storage Area used	Second Reference e Storage Area. Blank if RS used	*(Comma Delimited)*		
Input data for reference based on Difference in Stage.												
Fixed Start Date/Time	Date, Time											
The fixed start date and time or to use for the boundary condition data. Format is DDMMMYYYY, hhmm												

Key	1	2	3	4	5	6	7	8	9	10	11	12
Flow Hydrograph	Number of Flow Values											
	First Discharge in Hydrograph	Second Discharge in Hydrograph	(Continue for More discharge values. Ten discharges per line. Continues on next line(s) for more discharges)									
(The lines after Flow Hydrograph)			*(Fields of 8)*									

Number of flow values in the Flow Hydrograph. Tied to the boundary condition location above. Successive lines are the flow (discharge) values for the entire hydrograph.

Key	1	2	3	4	5	6	7	8	9	10	11	12
Flow Hydrograph Qmin	Minimum Flow											

Flow Hydrograph Minimum Flow. Tied to the boundary condition location above.

Key	1	2	3	4	5	6	7	8	9	10	11	12
Flow Hydrograph Qmult	Flow Hydrograph Multiplier											

Flow Hydrograph Multiplier. Tied to the boundary condition location above.

Key	1	2	3	4	5	6	7	8	9	10	11	12
Flow Title	Title of the Flow File											

Title of the Flow File

Key	1	2	3	4	5	6	7	8	9	10	11	12
Friction Slope	Friction Slope											

Slope for Normal Depth Computations, if selected. Tied to the boundary condition location above.

Key	1	2	3	4	5	6	7	8	9	10	11	12
Gate DSS Path	DSS Path											

For Time Series Gate Control. The DSS path for the gate opening data.

Key	1	2	3	4	5	6	7	8	9	10	11	12
Gate Fixed Start Date/Time	Date, Time											

For Time Series Gate Control. The fixed start date and time or to use for the time series gate control boundary condition data. Format is DDMMMYYYY, hhmm

Key	1	2	3	4	5	6	7	8	9	10	11	12
Gate Name	Gate Name											
For Time Series Gate Control. The Gate Name.												
Gate Openings	Number of Gate Opening Values											
			(Continue for More gate opening values. Ten gate openings per line. Continues on next line(s) for more gate openings)									
(The lines after Gate Openings)	First Gate Opening	Second Gate Opening		*(Fields of 8)*								
For Time Series Gate Control. The gate openings for the time series gate boundary condition.												
Gate Time Interval	Time Interval											
For Time Series Gate Control. Time interval for the gate opening time series data. This entry has a standard format, i.e. 6MIN, 2HOUR, 1DAY,1WEEK, etc.												
	True for "Use DSS", False otherwis e											
Gate Use DSS												
For Time Series Gate Control. Does this boundary condition use data from a DSS file?												
Gate Use Fixed Start Time	True for "Use Fixed Start Time, False											

Key	1	2	3	4	5	6	7	8	9	10	11	12
	otherwise											
For Time Series Gate Control. Tells HEC-RAS whether or not to use a fixed start time or to use simulation time for the time series gate control boundary condition data.												
		Length of the groundwater flow path										
Ground Water Darcy Distance												
Thickness (or length) of the groundwater interflow												
Ground Water Darcy K	Darcy K in K/hour units											
Darcy's K coefficient in K/hour units. This is not an input in the HEC-RAS GUI anywhere. It is computed by HEC-RAS based on the K/day input values. *Tied to the boundary condition location above.*												
Ground Water Darcy K/day	Darcy K in K/day units											
Darcy's K coefficient in K/day units. This value is entered by the user in the groundwater interflow editor. *Tied to the boundary condition location above.*												
Ground Water Interflow	Number of Flow Values											
	First Discharge in Hydrograph	Second Discharge in Hydrograph	(Continue for More discharge values. Ten discharges per line. Continues on next line(s) for more discharges)	(Fields of 8)								
(The lines after Flow Hydrograph)												
Number of flow values in a Groundwater Hydrograph. *Tied to the boundary condition location above.* Successive lines are the flow (discharge) values for the entire groundwater hydrograph.												

239

Key	1	2	3	4	5	6	7	8	9	10	11	12
Initial Flow Loc	River Name	Reach Name	River Station	Initial Flow Value	(Comma Delimited)							
Locations for initial flow values. Repeated for each initial flow location.												
Initial RRR Elev	River Name	Reach Name	River Station	Initial Stage	(Comma Delimited)							
Locations for Internal river station initial stages. Repeated for each initial stage location.												
Initial Storage Elev	Storage Area Name	Initial Elevation	(Comma Delimited)									
Locations for initial storage area elevations. Repeated for each initial storage area location.												
Interval	Time Interval											
Time between hydrograph points. Tied to the boundary condition location above. This entry has a standard format, i.e. 6MIN, 2HOUR, 1DAY,1WEEK, etc.												
Is Critical Boundary	True if checked, False if not checked											
Time Step Adjustment Options (i.e. "Time Slicing")												
Lateral Inflow Hydrograph	Number of Flow Values		(Continue for More discharge values. Ten discharges per line. Continues on next line(s) for more discharges)	(Fields of 8)								
(The lines after Lateral Inflow Hydrograph)	First Discharge in Hydrograph	Second Discharge in Hydrograph										
Number of flow values in the Lateral Inflow Hydrograph. Tied to the boundary condition location above. Successive lines are the flow (discharge) values for the entire lateral inflow hydrograph.												

Appendix D. The Unsteady Flow Input File Keys

Key	1	2	3	4	5	6	7	8	9	10	11	12
Navigation Dam	Normal gate change time increment	Rapidly varying flow gate change increment	Initial Gate Change Time	Gate Minimum Opening	Gate Opening Rate	Gate Closing Rate	Operation Type. 0 for Pool Only, 1 for Hinge Point Only, 2 for Hinge Point and Min Pool, 3 for Hinge Point and Min and Max Pool	Gate Maximum Opening	*(Comma Delimited)*			

For Navigation Dams boundary condition. Basic Input Data.

Key	1	2	3	4	5	6	7	8	9	10	11	12
Navigation Dam CP Hinge Point	Open River	Maximum High	Maximum	Target High	Target	Target Low	Minimum	Minimum Low	Close Gates	Flow Open River	Flow Factor Max	Flow Factor Target High
	13) Flow Factor Target Low	14) Flow Factor Min	15) Flow Minimum m	*(Comma Delimited)*								
(continued)												

For Navigation Dams boundary condition. Hinge Point Operations-Hinge Control inputs.

Key	1	2	3	4	5	6	7	8	9	10	11	12
Navigation Dam CP Max Pool	Open River	Maximum High	Maximum	Target High	Target	Target Low	Minimum	Minimum Low	Close Gates	Flow Open River	Flow Factor Max	Flow Factor Target High
	13) Flow Factor Target Low	14) Flow Factor Min	15) Flow Minimum m	*(Comma Delimited)*								
(continued)												

For Navigation Dams boundary condition. Max Pool Operations-Pool Control Inputs.

Key	1	2	3	4	5	6	7	8	9	10	11	12
Navigation Dam CP Min Pool	Open River	Maximum High	Maximum	Target High	Target	Target Low	Minimum	Minimum Low	Close Gates	Flow Open River	Flow Factor Max	Flow Factor Target High

Key	1	2	3	4	5	6	7	8	9	10	11	12
(continued)	13) Flow Factor Target Low	14) Flow Factor Min	15) Flow Minimum	(Comma Delimited)								

For Navigation Dams boundary condition. Min Pool Operations-Pool Control Inputs.

Key	1	2	3	4	5
Navigation Dam Flow Monitor RRR	Flow Monitor River	Flow Monitor Reach	Flow Monitor River Station	(Comma Delimited)	

For Navigation Dams boundary condition. Flow Monitor Reference Location(s). Can have up to three. Repeat key for each one.

Navigation Dam Hinge Point RRR	Hinge Control River	Hinge Control Reach	Hinge Control River Station	(Comma Delimited)	

For Navigation Dams boundary condition. Hinge Control Reference Location

Navigation Dam SFT	Number of Flow Profiles				
(The lines after **Navigation Dam SFT**)	Flow	Water Surface Max	Water Surface Min	(Continues on next line(s) for more profiles)	(Fields of 8)

For Navigation Dams boundary condition. Steady Profile Limits Table. Each flow in the table gets a corresponding Max and Min water surface elevation.

Observed DSS Dn Dist	Distance				

The distance downstream of the referenced river station where the observed data was taken.

Observed DSS Filename	DSS Filename				

The file name of the dss file used for the observed data.

Observed DSS Loc	River	Reach	River Station	(Comma Delimited)	

The river, reach and river station of the observed data.

Observed DSS Pathname	DSS Pathname for the observed data				

Appendix D. The Unsteady Flow Input File Keys

Key	1	2	3	4	5	6	7	8	9	10	11	12
The path for the observed data												
Observed HWM	River	Reach	River Station	Downstream Distance	High Water Elevation	(Comma Delimited)						
High water marks for a given river station.												
Observed Stage and Flow Hydrograph	Number of Stage/Flow Pairs											
(The lines after Observed Stage and Flow Hydrograph)	First Stage	First Discharge	Second Stage	Second Discharge	Third Stage	Third Discharge	(Continue for More stage and discharge values. Ten pairs per line. Continues on next line(s) for more pairs)	(Fields of 8)				
IB Stage/Flow Boundary. Number of stage/flow pairs in the observed Stage and Flow data. Tied to the boundary condition location above. Successive lines are the stage/flow values for the entire observed data record.												
Program Version	HEC-RAS Version											
Version of HEC-RAS the Unsteady Flow File was last saved by.												
Rating Curve	Number of stage/flow pairs											
(The lines after Rating Curve)	First Stage	First Flow	Second Stage	Second Flow	Third Stage	Third Flow	Fourth Stage	Fourth Flow	Fifth Stage	Fifth Flow	(Continue on next line(s) for more stage/flow pairs)	(Fields of 8)
Rating Curve boundary condition. The Key line includes the number of stage flow pairs that make up the rating curve. Successive line(s) are used for the stage/flow pairs. Tied to the boundary condition location above.												

Key	1	2	3	4	5	6	7	8	9	10	11	12
Restart Filename	Filename of the restart file.											

File name of the restart file.

Key	1	2	3	4	5	6	7	8	9	10	11	12
Uniform Lateral Inflow Hydrograph	Number of Flow Values											
			(Continue for More discharge values. Ten discharges per line. Continues on next line(s) for more discharges)									
(The lines after Lateral Inflow Hydrograph)	First Discharge in Hydrograph	Second Discharge in Hydrograph		*(Fields of 8)*								

Number of flow values in the Uniform Lateral Inflow Hydrograph. Tied to the boundary condition location above. Successive lines are the flow (discharge) values for the entire uniform lateral inflow hydrograph.

Key	1	2	3	4	5	6	7	8	9	10	11	12
Use DSS	True for "Use DSS", False otherwise											

Tells HEC-RAS whether or not to use a DSS file or user-entered data for the boundary condition. Tied to the boundary condition location above.

Key	1	2	3	4	5	6	7	8	9	10	11	12
Use Fixed Start Time	True for "Use Fixed Start Time, False otherwise											

Tells HEC-RAS whether or not to use a fixed start time or to use simulation time for the boundary condition data.

Appendix D. The Unsteady Flow Input File Keys

Key	1	2	3	4	5	6	7	8	9	10	11	12
	0 for Enter Initial Flow Distribution, -1 for Use a Restart File											
Use Restart												

Directs RAS to use a restart file or initial flow distribution.

APPENDIX E. HEC-RAS OUTPUT VARIABLES

The following tables contains all of the output variables available in HEC-RAS. The number preceding the variable name is the index number to be used as the argument for the **nVar** parameter in the **Output_NodeOutput** and **Output_ReachOutput** procedures.

Table 8 lists all of the variables ordered by their respective ID numbers. *Table 9* lists the same variables, only ordered alphabetically, for convenience.

Table 8. HEC-RAS Variable Names by ID Number.

RAS ID	Variable	Description
1	Profile	Profile number.
2	W.S. Elev	Calculated water surface from energy equation.
3	E.G. Elev	Energy gradeline for given WSEL.
4	Max Chl Dpth	Maximum main channel depth.
5	Min Ch El	Minimum channel elevation.
6	Q Left	Flow in left overbank.
7	Q Channel	Flow in main channel.
8	Q Right	Flow in right overbank.
9	Q Total	Total flow in cross section.
10	Flow Area	Total area of cross section active flow.
11	Flow Area L	Area of left overbank active flow.
12	Flow Area Ch	Area of main channel active flow.
13	Flow Area R	Area of right overbank active flow.
14	W.P. Total	Wetted perimeter of total cross section.
15	W.P. Left	Wetted perimeter of left overbank.

16	W.P. Channel	Wetted perimeter of main channel.
17	W.P. Right	Wetted perimeter of right overbank.
18	Conv. Total	Conveyance of total cross section.
19	Conv. Left	Conveyance of left overbank.
20	Conv. Chnl	Conveyance of main channel.
21	Conv. Right	Conveyance of right overbank.
22	Vel Head	Velocity head.
23	Vel Total	Average velocity of flow in total cross section.
24	Vel Left	Average velocity of flow in left overbank.
25	Vel Chnl	Average velocity of flow in main channel.
26	Vel Right	Average velocity of flow in right overbank.
27	Alpha	Alpha - energy weighting coefficient.
28	Beta	Beta - momentum weighting coefficient.
29	Top Wdth Act	Top width of the wetted cross section, not including ineffective flow.
30	E.G. Slope	Slope of the energy grade line at a cross section.
31	Volume	Cumulative volume of water from the downstream end of the reach (including ineffective areas).
32	Area	Flow area of the entire cross section including ineffective flow.
33	Area Left	Flow area of the left overbank including ineffective flow.
34	Area Channel	Flow area of the main channel including ineffective flow.
35	Area Right	Flow area of the right overbank including ineffective flow.
36	Sta W.S. Lft	Left station where water intersects the ground.
37	Sta W.S. Rgt	Right station where water intersects the ground.
38	Left Sta Eff	Furthest left station where there is effective flow.
39	Rght Sta Eff	Furthest right station that still has effective flow.
40	Length Wtd.	Weighted length based on flow distribution, in left bank, channel, and right bank.
41	Length Left	Downstream reach length of the left overbank.
42	Length Chnl	Downstream reach length of the main channel to next XS (unless BR is d/s, then this is the distance to the deck/roadway).
43	Length Rght	Downstream reach length of the right overbank.
44	Mann Wtd Left	Conveyance weighted Manning's n for the left overbank.
45	Mann Wtd Chnl	Conveyance weighted Manning's n for the main channel.
46	Mann Wtd Rght	Conveyance weighted Manning's n for the right overbank.
47	Mann Comp	Manning's n value for main channel based on composite roughness equation.
48	Froude # Chl	Froude number for the main channel.
49	Froude # XS	Froude number for the entire cross section.

50	Trvl Tme Avg	Cumulative travel time based on the average velocity of the entire cross section per reach.
51	Trvl Tme Chl	Cumulative travel time based on the average velocity of the main channel per reach.
52	Conv. Ratio	Ratio of the conveyance of the current cross section to the conveyance of the downstream cross section.
53	Specif Force	The specific force for this cross section at the computed water surface elevation.
54	Spc Force PR	Specific force prime. For mixed flow, the specific force at this cross section for the flow regime that does not control.
55	W.S. Prime	Water surface prime. For mixed flow, the water surface of the flow regime that does not control.
56	Crit W.S.	Critical water surface elevation. Water surface corresponding to the minimum energy on the energy versus depth curve.
57	Crit E.G.	Critical energy elevation. Minimum energy on the energy versus depth curve.
58	Crit Depth	Critical depth. Corresponds to critical water surface.
59	Frctn Loss	Friction loss between two cross sections.
60	C & E Loss	Contraction or expansion loss between two cross sections.
61	Headloss	Total energy loss between two cross sections.
62	Top Width	Top width of the wetted cross section.
63	Top W Left	Top width of the left overbank. Does not include `islands', but it does include ineffective flow.
64	Top W Chnl	Top width of the main channel. Does not include `islands', but it does include ineffective flow.
65	Top W Right	Top width of the right overbank. Does not include `islands', but it does include ineffective flow.
66	Num Trials	Current number (or final number) of trials attempted before the energy equation is balanced.
67	Std Stp Case	Standard step method used to determine WSEL (1 = successful convergence, 2 = minimum error, 3 = resorted to critical depth).
68	Frctn Slope	Representative friction slope between two cross sections.
69	Frctn Slp Md	Friction slope averaging method used.
70	Min Error	The minimum error, between the calculated and assumed water surfaces when balancing the energy equation.
71	Delta WS	Change in water surface through culvert(s) and Bridge(s).
72	Delta EG	Change in energy grade line through culvert(s) and Bridge(s).
73	Q Culv Group	Flow through all barrels in a culvert.
74	Q Barrel	Flow through one barrel in a culvert.

75	W.S. US.	Upstream water surface elevation upstream of bridge, culvert or weir (specific to that opening, not necessarily the energy weighted average).
76	Clv EG No Wr	Energy grade elevation at the culvert that was calculated without the weir.
77	E.G. US.	Upstream energy grade elevation at bridge or culvert (specific to that opening, not necessarily the weighted average).
78	E.G. IC	Upstream energy gradeline based on inlet control.
79	E.G. OC	Upstream energy gradeline based on outlet control.
80	Culv Nml Depth	Normal depth for this culvert (and flow).
81	Culv Vel DS	Velocity in culvert at defined downstream.
82	Culv Vel US	Velocity in culvert at defined upstream.
83	Culv Frctn Ls	Friction loss through the culvert.
84	Culv Entr Loss	Entrance loss (energy loss due only to entrance).
85	Culv Exit Loss	Exit loss (energy loss due to exit).
86	Culv Full Len	The length that the culvert flows full.
87	Culv Crt Depth	Critical depth inside the culvert.
88	Culv Inv El Up	Culvert invert elevation upstream.
89	Culv Inv El Dn	Culvert invert elevation downstream.
90	Culv EG Inlet	Energy gradeline inside the culvert at the inlet.
91	Culv EG Outlet	Energy gradeline inside the culvert at the outlet.
92	Culv WS Inlet	Water surface elevation inside the culvert at the inlet.
93	Culv WS Outlet	Water surface elevation inside the culvert at the outlet.
94	Q Weir	Flow over the weir.
95	Weir Flow Area	Area of the flow going over the weir.
96	Weir Sta Lft	Station where flow starts on the left side.
97	Weir Sta Rgt	Station where flow ends on the right side.
98	Weir Max Depth	The maximum depth over the weir.
99	Weir Avg Depth	The average depth over the weir.
100	Weir Submerg	The ratio of the downstream depth above the weir to the upstream depth above the weir.
101	Min El Weir Flow	Elevation where weir flow begins.
102	Wr Top Wdth	Top width of water over the weir.
103	Energy/Wr WS	Water surface elevation upstream of bridge for low flow energy method and weir flow.
104	Yarnell WS	Water surface elevation upstream of bridge for Yarnell method.
105	WSPRO WS	Water surface elevation upstream of bridge for the WSPRO method.
106	Prs/Wr WS	Water surface elevation upstream of bridge for pressure and/or weir method.
107	Energy WS	Water surface elevation upstream of bridge for energy only method.

108	Momen. WS	Water surface elevation upstream of bridge for momentum method.
109	Prs O WS	Water surface elevation upstream of bridge for pressure only method.
110	Energy/Wr EG	Energy grade elevation upstream of bridge for energy method.
111	Yarnell EG	Energy grade elevation upstream of bridge for Yarnell method.
112	WSPRO EG	Energy grade elevation upstream of bridge for the WSPRO method.
113	Prs/Wr EG	Energy grade elevation upstream of bridge for pressure and/or weir method.
114	Energy EG	Energy grade elevation upstream of bridge for energy only method.
115	Momen. EG	Energy grade elevation upstream of bridge for momentum method.
116	Prs O EG	Energy grade elevation upstream of bridge for pressure only method.
117	Br Sel Method	Selected bridge method.
118	Min El Prs	Elevation at the bridge when pressure flow begins.
119	Crit Num	Number of critical depths found.
120	Crit W.S. 1	Water surface elevation of first critical depth.
121	Crit W.S. 2	Water surface elevation of second critical depth.
122	Crit W.S. 3	Water surface elevation of third critical depth.
123	Crit Enrgy 1	Energy associated with first critical depth.
124	Crit Enrgy 2	Energy associated with second critical depth.
125	Crit Enrgy 3	Energy associated with third critical depth.
126	Hydr Depth	Hydraulic depth for cross section.
127	Hydr Depth L	Hydraulic depth in left over bank.
128	Hydr Depth C	Hydraulic depth in channel.
129	Hydr Depth R	Hydraulic depth for right over bank.
130	Deck Width	Width of Deck.
131	# Barrels	Number of barrels in a culvert.
132	Q Bridge	Flow through a bridge opening.
133	Vol Left	Cumulative volume of water in the left overbank from the downstream end of the reach (including ineffective areas).
134	Vol Chan	Cumulative volume of water in the channel from the downstream end of the reach (including ineffective areas).
135	Vol Right	Cumulative volume of water in the right overbank from the downstream end of the reach (including ineffective areas).
136	Min El	Minimum overall section elevation.
137	Enc Val 1	Target for encroachment analysis.

138	Enc Val 2	Second target for encroachment analysis.
139	Enc Sta L	Left station of encroachment.
140	Enc Sta R	Right station of encroachment.
141	Dist Center L	Distance from center of channel to left encroachment.
142	Dist Center R	Distance from center of channel to right encroachment.
143	K Perc L	Conveyance reduction from left encroachment.
144	K Perc R	Conveyance reduction from right encroachment.
145	Q Perc L	Percent of flow in left overbank.
146	Q Perc Chan	Percent of flow in main channel.
147	Q Perc R	Percent of flow in right overbank.
148	Prof Delta WS	Difference in WS between current profile and WS for first profile.
149	Prof Delta EG	Difference in EG between current profile and EG for first profile.
150	Shear Total	Shear stress in total section.
151	Shear LOB	Shear stress in left overbank.
152	Shear Chan	Shear stress in main channel.
153	Shear ROB	Shear stress in right overbank.
154	Power Total	Total stream power.
155	Power LOB	Total stream power in left overbank.
156	Power Chan	Total stream power in main channel.
157	Power ROB	Total stream power in right overbank.
158	Ch Sta L	Left station of channel.
159	Ch Sta R	Right station of channel.
160	Base WS	Water surface for first profile (used in comparison of encroachments).
161	Center Station	Center station of main channel.
162	XS Delta WS	Change in water surface between current section and next one downstream.
163	XS Delta EG	Change in energy gradeline between current section and next one downstream.
164	SA Total	Cumulative surface area for entire cross section (including ineffective areas) from the downstream end of the reach.
165	SA Left	Cumulative surface area for left overbank (including ineffective areas) from the downstream end of the reach.
166	SA Chan	Cumulative surface area for main channel (including ineffective areas) from the downstream end of the reach.
167	SA Right	Cumulative surface area for right overbank (including ineffective areas) from the downstream end of the reach.
168	Enc Method	Encroachment method.
169	Q Gate Group	Flow through all gate openings in a gate group.
170	Gate Open Ht	Height of gate opening.
171	Gate #Open	The number of gates opened in the current group.

172	Gate Area	The flow area in an opened gate.
173	Gate Submerg	The ratio of the downstream depth above the gate to the upstream depth above the gate.
174	Gate Invert	Gate spillway invert elevation.
175	Q Gates	Total flow through all of the gate groups of an inline/lateral structure.
176	BR Open Area	Total area of the entire bridge opening.
177	Coef of Q	WSPRO bridge method coefficient of discharge.
178	Cum Ch Len	Cumulative Channel Length from the downstream end of the reach.
179	Enc WD	Encroachment Width.
180	Obs WS	Observed Water Surface.
181	WS Air Entr.	Water surface elevation accounting for air entrainment.
182	BR Open Vel	Average velocity inside the bridge opening (Maximum of BU and BD).
183	Ice Thick LOB	Ice thickness in the left overbank.
184	Ice Thick Chan	Ice thickness in the main channel.
185	Ice Thick ROB	Ice thickness in the right overbank.
186	Ice Vol Total	Cumulative volume of ice in an ice jam.
187	Ice Vol. LOB	Cumulative volume of ice in the left overbank for an ice jam.
188	Ice Vol. Chan	Cumulative volume of ice in the main channel for an ice jam.
189	Ice Vol. ROB	Cumulative volume of ice in the right overbank for an ice jam.
190	Ice Top LOB	The top elevation of ice in the left overbank.
191	Ice Top Chan	The top elevation of ice in the main channel.
192	Ice Top ROB	The top elevation of ice in the right overbank.
193	Ice Btm LOB	The bottom elevation of ice in the left overbank.
194	Ice Btm Chan	The bottom elevation of ice in the main channel.
195	Ice Btm ROB	The bottom elevation of ice in the right overbank.
196	Invert Slope	The slope from the invert of this cross section to the next cross section downstream.
197	LOB Elev	The ground elevation at the left bank of the main channel.
198	ROB Elev	The ground elevation at the right bank of the main channel.
199	L. Freeboard	The freeboard in the main channel at the left bank.
200	R. Freeboard	The freeboard in the main channel at the right bank.
201	Levee El Left	The elevation of the left levee.
202	Levee El Right	The elevation of the right levee.
203	Ineff El Left	The elevation of the left ineffective area.
204	Ineff El Right	The elevation of the right ineffective area.
205	L. Levee Frbrd	The freeboard before the left levee is over-topped.

206	R. Levee Frbrd	The freeboard before the right levee is over-topped.
207	Mann Wtd Total	Manning's n value for the total main cross section.
208	Hydr Radius	Hydraulic radius for cross section.
209	Hydr Radius L	Hydraulic radius in left over bank.
210	Hydr Radius C	Hydraulic radius in channel.
211	Hydr Radius R	Hydraulic radius for right over bank.
212	Hydr Rad 2/3	Hydraulic radius for cross section to the 2/3 power.
213	W.S. DS	Water surface downstream.
214	E.G. DS	Energy elevation downstream.
215	Min Weir El	Minimum weir elevation.
216	Perc Q Leaving	Percentage of flow leaving through a lateral structure.
217	Q US	Flow in cross section upstream of a lateral structure.
218	Q DS	Flow in cross section downstream of lateral structure.
219	Weir Sta US	Upstream station for weir flow starts.
220	Weir Sta DS	Downstream station where weir flow ends.
221	Q Leaving Total	Total flow leaving in a lateral structure including all gates, culverts and lateral rating curves.
222	SA Min El	Minimum elevation of a storage area.
223	SA Area	Surface area of a storage area.
224	SA Volume	Storage volume of a storage area.
225	Top W Act Left	Top width of the wetted left bank, not including ineffective flow.
226	Top W Act Chan	Top width of the wetted channel, not including ineffective flow.
227	Top W Act Right	Top width of the wetted right bank, not including ineffective flow.
228	Culv Depth Blocked	Depth of fill in a culvert.
229	Culv Inlet Mann n	The composite n value at the culvert inlet.
230	Culv Outlet Mann n	The composite n value at the culvert outlet.
231	Ice WS Err	Convergence error in water surface for dynamic ice jam.
232	Ice Err	Convergence error in ice thickness for dynamic ice jam.
233	Piping Flow	Flow from piping weir failure.
234	Breach CL	Center line of weir breach.
235	Breach WD	Bottom width of weir breach.
236	Breach Bottom El	Bottom Elevation of weir breach.
237	Breach Top El	Top Elevation of weir breach.
238	Breach SSL	Left side slope of weir breach.
239	Breach SSR	Right side slope of weir breach.
240	Q Pump Group	Pump group flow.
241	Q Lat RC	Lateral rating curve flow.
242	Q Culv	Total flow in all culvert groups.

243	Culv Length	Length of the culvert barrel.
244	Q Pump Station	Total flow in all pump groups in a pump station.
245	WS Inlet	WS at the inlet of a pump station.
246	WS Outlet	WS at the outlet of a pump station.
247	Pumping Head	Pumping head for the pump station.
248	Inflow	Net inflow into a storage area.
249	Outflow	Net outflow into a storage area.
250	Net Flux	Net inflow - outflow for a storage area.
251	Enc Offset L	Minimum setback from the left overbank station.
252	Enc Offset R	Minimum setback from the right overbank station.
253	Min Ch Pilot	Minimum channel elevation (including pilot channels).
254	Diff	Difference between the previous two columns.
255	Min Ch El Sta	Station of the minimum channel elevation.
256	Culv Area DS	Cross sectional flow area in culvert at defined downstream.
257	Culv Area US	Cross sectional flow area in culvert at defined upstream.
258	Gate Weir Coef	Coefficient used in weir flow over the gate.
259	Weir Coef	Coefficient used in weir flow.
260	Q Breach	Flow through a breach.
261	Breach Avg Velocity	Average flow velocity through a breach.
262	Breach Flow Area	Flow area through a breach.
263	Left Station	Left station of the cross section.
264	Right Station	Right station of the cross section.
265	Levee Sta Left	Left levee station.
266	Levee Sta Right	Right levee station.
267	Q Inline RC	Inline Outlet rating curve flow.
268	Q Outlet TS	Inline/Lateral Outlet time series flow.

Table 9. HEC-RAS Variable Names Alphabetically.

Variable	RAS ID	Description
# Barrels	131	Number of barrels in a culvert.
Alpha	27	Alpha - energy weighting coefficient.
Area	32	Flow area of the entire cross section including ineffective flow.
Area Channel	34	Flow area of the main channel including ineffective flow.
Area Left	33	Flow area of the left overbank including ineffective flow.
Area Right	35	Flow area of the right overbank including ineffective flow.
Base WS	160	Water surface for first profile (used in comparison of encroachments).
Beta	28	Beta - momentum weighting coefficient.
BR Open Area	176	Total area of the entire bridge opening.
BR Open Vel	182	Average velocity inside the bridge opening (Maximum of BU and BD).
Br Sel Method	117	Selected bridge method.
Breach Avg Velocity	261	Average flow velocity through a breach.
Breach Bottom El	236	Bottom Elevation of weir breach.
Breach CL	234	Center line of weir breach.
Breach Flow Area	262	Flow area through a breach.
Breach SSL	238	Left side slope of weir breach.
Breach SSR	239	Right side slope of weir breach.
Breach Top El	237	Top Elevation of weir breach.
Breach WD	235	Bottom width of weir breach.
C & E Loss	60	Contraction or expansion loss between two cross sections.
Center Station	161	Center station of main channel.
Ch Sta L	158	Left station of channel.
Ch Sta R	159	Right station of channel.
Clv EG No Wr	76	Energy grade elevation at the culvert that was calculated without the weir.
Coef of Q	177	WSPRO bridge method coefficient of discharge.
Conv. Chnl	20	Conveyance of main channel.
Conv. Left	19	Conveyance of left overbank.
Conv. Ratio	52	Ratio of the conveyance of the current cross section to the conveyance of the downstream cross section.
Conv. Right	21	Conveyance of right overbank.
Conv. Total	18	Conveyance of total cross section.
Crit Depth	58	Critical depth. Corresponds to critical water surface.
Crit E.G.	57	Critical energy elevation. Minimum energy on the energy versus depth curve.
Crit Enrgy 1	123	Energy associated with first critical depth.

Crit Enrgy 2	124	Energy associated with second critical depth.
Crit Enrgy 3	125	Energy associated with third critical depth.
Crit Num	119	Number of critical depths found.
Crit W.S.	56	Critical water surface elevation. Water surface corresponding to the minimum energy on the energy versus depth curve.
Crit W.S. 1	120	Water surface elevation of first critical depth.
Crit W.S. 2	121	Water surface elevation of second critical depth.
Crit W.S. 3	122	Water surface elevation of third critical depth.
Culv Area DS	256	Cross sectional flow area in culvert at defined downstream.
Culv Area US	257	Cross sectional flow area in culvert at defined upstream.
Culv Crt Depth	87	Critical depth inside the culvert.
Culv Depth Blocked	228	Depth of fill in a culvert.
Culv EG Inlet	90	Energy gradeline inside the culvert at the inlet.
Culv EG Outlet	91	Energy gradeline inside the culvert at the outlet.
Culv Entr Loss	84	Entrance loss (energy loss due only to entrance).
Culv Exit Loss	85	Exit loss (energy loss due to exit).
Culv Frctn Ls	83	Friction loss through the culvert.
Culv Full Len	86	The length that the culvert flows full.
Culv Inlet Mann n	229	The composite n value at the culvert inlet.
Culv Inv El Dn	89	Culvert invert elevation downstream.
Culv Inv El Up	88	Culvert invert elevation upstream.
Culv Length	243	Length of the culvert barrel.
Culv Nml Depth	80	Normal depth for this culvert (and flow).
Culv Outlet Mann n	230	The composite n value at the culvert outlet.
Culv Vel DS	81	Velocity in culvert at defined downstream.
Culv Vel US	82	Velocity in culvert at defined upstream.
Culv WS Inlet	92	Water surface elevation inside the culvert at the inlet.
Culv WS Outlet	93	Water surface elevation inside the culvert at the outlet.
Cum Ch Len	178	Cumulative Channel Length from the downstream end of the reach.
Deck Width	130	Width of Deck.
Delta EG	72	Change in energy grade line through culvert(s) and Bridge(s).
Delta WS	71	Change in water surface through culvert(s) and Bridge(s).
Diff	254	Difference between the previous two columns.
Dist Center L	141	Distance from center of channel to left encroachment.
Dist Center R	142	Distance from center of channel to right encroachment.
E.G. DS	214	Energy elevation downstream.
E.G. Elev	3	Energy gradeline for given WSEL.
E.G. IC	78	Upstream energy gradeline based on inlet control.
E.G. OC	79	Upstream energy gradeline based on outlet control.

E.G. Slope	30	Slope of the energy grade line at a cross section.
E.G. US.	77	Upstream energy grade elevation at bridge or culvert (specific to that opening, not necessarily the weighted average).
Enc Method	168	Encroachment method.
Enc Offset L	251	Minimum setback from the left overbank station.
Enc Offset R	252	Minimum setback from the right overbank station.
Enc Sta L	139	Left station of encroachment.
Enc Sta R	140	Right station of encroachment.
Enc Val 1	137	Target for encroachment analysis.
Enc Val 2	138	Second target for encroachment analysis.
Enc WD	179	Encroachment Width.
Energy EG	114	Energy grade elevation upstream of bridge for energy only method.
Energy WS	107	Water surface elevation upstream of bridge for energy only method.
Energy/Wr EG	110	Energy grade elevation upstream of bridge for energy method.
Energy/Wr WS	103	Water surface elevation upstream of bridge for low flow energy method and weir flow.
Flow Area	10	Total area of cross section active flow.
Flow Area Ch	12	Area of main channel active flow.
Flow Area L	11	Area of left overbank active flow.
Flow Area R	13	Area of right overbank active flow.
Frctn Loss	59	Friction loss between two cross sections.
Frctn Slope	68	Representative friction slope between two cross sections.
Frctn Slp Md	69	Friction slope averaging method used.
Froude # Chl	48	Froude number for the main channel.
Froude # XS	49	Froude number for the entire cross section.
Gate #Open	171	The number of gates opened in the current group.
Gate Area	172	The flow area in an opened gate.
Gate Invert	174	Gate spillway invert elevation.
Gate Open Ht	170	Height of gate opening.
Gate Submerg	173	The ratio of the downstream depth above the gate to the upstream depth above the gate.
Gate Weir Coef	258	Coefficient used in weir flow over the gate.
Headloss	61	Total energy loss between two cross sections.
Hydr Depth	126	Hydraulic depth for cross section.
Hydr Depth C	128	Hydraulic depth in channel.
Hydr Depth L	127	Hydraulic depth in left over bank.
Hydr Depth R	129	Hydraulic depth for right over bank.
Hydr Rad 2/3	212	Hydraulic radius for cross section to the 2/3 power.
Hydr Radius	208	Hydraulic radius for cross section.

Hydr Radius C	210	Hydraulic radius in channel.
Hydr Radius L	209	Hydraulic radius in left over bank.
Hydr Radius R	211	Hydraulic radius for right over bank.
Ice Btm Chan	194	The bottom elevation of ice in the main channel.
Ice Btm LOB	193	The bottom elevation of ice in the left overbank.
Ice Btm ROB	195	The bottom elevation of ice in the right overbank.
Ice Err	232	Convergence error in ice thickness for dynamic ice jam.
Ice Thick Chan	184	Ice thickness in the main channel.
Ice Thick LOB	183	Ice thickness in the left overbank.
Ice Thick ROB	185	Ice thickness in the right overbank.
Ice Top Chan	191	The top elevation of ice in the main channel.
Ice Top LOB	190	The top elevation of ice in the left overbank.
Ice Top ROB	192	The top elevation of ice in the right overbank.
Ice Vol Total	186	Cumulative volume of ice in an ice jam.
Ice Vol. Chan	188	Cumulative volume of ice in the main channel for an ice jam.
Ice Vol. LOB	187	Cumulative volume of ice in the left overbank for an ice jam.
Ice Vol. ROB	189	Cumulative volume of ice in the right overbank for an ice jam.
Ice WS Err	231	Convergence error in water surface for dynamic ice jam.
Ineff El Left	203	The elevation of the left ineffective area.
Ineff El Right	204	The elevation of the right ineffective area.
Inflow	248	Net inflow into a storage area.
Invert Slope	196	The slope from the invert of this cross section to the next cross section downstream.
K Perc L	143	Conveyance reduction from left encroachment.
K Perc R	144	Conveyance reduction from right encroachment.
L. Freeboard	199	The freeboard in the main channel at the left bank.
L. Levee Frbrd	205	The freeboard before the left levee is over-topped.
Left Sta Eff	38	Furthest left station where there is effective flow.
Left Station	263	Left station of the cross section.
Length Chnl	42	Downstream reach length of the main channel to next XS (unless BR is d/s, then this is the distance to the deck/roadway).
Length Left	41	Downstream reach length of the left overbank.
Length Rght	43	Downstream reach length of the right overbank.
Length Wtd.	40	Weighted length based on flow distribution, in left bank, channel, and right bank.
Levee El Left	201	The elevation of the left levee.
Levee El Right	202	The elevation of the right levee.
Levee Sta Left	265	Left levee station.
Levee Sta Right	266	Right levee station.

LOB Elev	197	The ground elevation at the left bank of the main channel.
Mann Comp	47	Manning's n value for main channel based on composite roughness equation.
Mann Wtd Chnl	45	Conveyance weighted Manning's n for the main channel.
Mann Wtd Left	44	Conveyance weighted Manning's n for the left overbank.
Mann Wtd Rght	46	Conveyance weighted Manning's n for the right overbank.
Mann Wtd Total	207	Manning's n value for the total main cross section.
Max Chl Dpth	4	Maximum main channel depth.
Min Ch El	5	Minimum channel elevation.
Min Ch El Sta	255	Station of the minimum channel elevation.
Min Ch Pilot	253	Minimum channel elevation (including pilot channels).
Min El	136	Minimum overall section elevation.
Min El Prs	118	Elevation at the bridge when pressure flow begins.
Min El Weir Flow	101	Elevation where weir flow begins.
Min Error	70	The minimum error, between the calculated and assumed water surfaces when balancing the energy equation.
Min Weir El	215	Minimum weir elevation.
Momen. EG	115	Energy grade elevation upstream of bridge for momentum method.
Momen. WS	108	Water surface elevation upstream of bridge for momentum method.
Net Flux	250	Net inflow - outflow for a storage area.
Num Trials	66	Current number (or final number) of trials attempted before the energy equation is balanced.
Obs WS	180	Observed Water Surface.
Outflow	249	Net outflow into a storage area.
Perc Q Leaving	216	Percentage of flow leaving through a lateral structure.
Piping Flow	233	Flow from piping weir failure.
Power Chan	156	Total stream power in main channel.
Power LOB	155	Total stream power in left overbank.
Power ROB	157	Total stream power in right overbank.
Power Total	154	Total stream power.
Prof Delta EG	149	Difference in EG between current profile and EG for first profile.
Prof Delta WS	148	Difference in WS between current profile and WS for first profile.
Profile	1	Profile number.
Prs O EG	116	Energy grade elevation upstream of bridge for pressure only method.
Prs O WS	109	Water surface elevation upstream of bridge for pressure only method.

Prs/Wr EG	113	Energy grade elevation upstream of bridge for pressure and/or weir method.
Prs/Wr WS	106	Water surface elevation upstream of bridge for pressure and/or weir method.
Pumping Head	247	Pumping head for the pump station.
Q Barrel	74	Flow through one barrel in a culvert.
Q Breach	260	Flow through a breach.
Q Bridge	132	Flow through a bridge opening.
Q Channel	7	Flow in main channel.
Q Culv	242	Total flow in all culvert groups.
Q Culv Group	73	Flow through all barrels in a culvert.
Q DS	218	Flow in cross section downstream of lateral structure.
Q Gate Group	169	Flow through all gate openings in a gate group.
Q Gates	175	Total flow through all of the gate groups of an inline/lateral structure.
Q Inline RC	267	Inline Outlet rating curve flow.
Q Lat RC	241	Lateral rating curve flow.
Q Leaving Total	221	Total flow leaving in a lateral structure including all gates, culverts and lateral rating curves.
Q Left	6	Flow in left overbank.
Q Outlet TS	268	Inline/Lateral Outlet time series flow.
Q Perc Chan	146	Percent of flow in main channel.
Q Perc L	145	Percent of flow in left overbank.
Q Perc R	147	Percent of flow in right overbank.
Q Pump Group	240	Pump group flow.
Q Pump Station	244	Total flow in all pump groups in a pump station.
Q Right	8	Flow in right overbank.
Q Total	9	Total flow in cross section.
Q US	217	Flow in cross section upstream of a lateral structure.
Q Weir	94	Flow over the weir.
R. Freeboard	200	The freeboard in the main channel at the right bank.
R. Levee Frbrd	206	The freeboard before the right levee is over-topped.
Rght Sta Eff	39	Furthest right station that still has effective flow.
Right Station	264	Right station of the cross section.
ROB Elev	198	The ground elevation at the right bank of the main channel.
SA Area	223	Surface area of a storage area.
SA Chan	166	Cumulative surface area for main channel (including ineffective areas) from the downstream end of the reach.
SA Left	165	Cumulative surface area for left overbank (including ineffective areas) from the downstream end of the reach.
SA Min El	222	Minimum elevation of a storage area.

SA Right	167	Cumulative surface area for right overbank (including ineffective areas) from the downstream end of the reach.
SA Total	164	Cumulative surface area for entire cross section (including ineffective areas) from the downstream end of the reach.
SA Volume	224	Storage volume of a storage area.
Shear Chan	152	Shear stress in main channel.
Shear LOB	151	Shear stress in left overbank.
Shear ROB	153	Shear stress in right overbank.
Shear Total	150	Shear stress in total section.
Spc Force PR	54	Specific force prime. For mixed flow, the specific force at this cross section for the flow regime that does not control.
Specif Force	53	The specific force for this cross section at the computed water surface elevation.
Sta W.S. Lft	36	Left station where water intersects the ground.
Sta W.S. Rgt	37	Right station where water intersects the ground.
Std Stp Case	67	Standard step method used to determine WSEL (1 = successful convergence, 2 = minimum error, 3 = resorted to critical depth).
Top W Act Chan	226	Top width of the wetted channel, not including ineffective flow.
Top W Act Left	225	Top width of the wetted left bank, not including ineffective flow.
Top W Act Right	227	Top width of the wetted right bank, not including ineffective flow.
Top W Chnl	64	Top width of the main channel. Does not include `islands', but it does include ineffective flow.
Top W Left	63	Top width of the left overbank. Does not include `islands', but it does include ineffective flow.
Top W Right	65	Top width of the right overbank. Does not include `islands', but it does include ineffective flow.
Top Wdth Act	29	Top width of the wetted cross section, not including ineffective flow.
Top Width	62	Top width of the wetted cross section.
Trvl Tme Avg	50	Cumulative travel time based on the average velocity of the entire cross section per reach.
Trvl Tme Chl	51	Cumulative travel time based on the average velocity of the main channel per reach.
Vel Chnl	25	Average velocity of flow in main channel.
Vel Head	22	Velocity head.
Vel Left	24	Average velocity of flow in left overbank.
Vel Right	26	Average velocity of flow in right overbank.
Vel Total	23	Average velocity of flow in total cross section.

Vol Chan	134	Cumulative volume of water in the channel from the downstream end of the reach (including ineffective areas).
Vol Left	133	Cumulative volume of water in the left overbank from the downstream end of the reach (including ineffective areas).
Vol Right	135	Cumulative volume of water in the right overbank from the downstream end of the reach (including ineffective areas).
Volume	31	Cumulative volume of water from the downstream end of the reach (including ineffective areas).
W.P. Channel	16	Wetted perimeter of main channel.
W.P. Left	15	Wetted perimeter of left overbank.
W.P. Right	17	Wetted perimeter of right overbank.
W.P. Total	14	Wetted perimeter of total cross section.
W.S. DS	213	Water surface downstream.
W.S. Elev	2	Calculated water surface from energy equation.
W.S. Prime	55	Water surface prime. For mixed flow, the water surface of the flow regime that does not control.
W.S. US.	75	Upstream water surface elevation upstream of bridge, culvert or weir (specific to that opening, not necessarily the energy weighted average).
Weir Avg Depth	99	The average depth over the weir.
Weir Coef	259	Coefficient used in weir flow.
Weir Flow Area	95	Area of the flow going over the weir.
Weir Max Depth	98	The maximum depth over the weir.
Weir Sta DS	220	Downstream station where weir flow ends.
Weir Sta Lft	96	Station where flow starts on the left side.
Weir Sta Rgt	97	Station where flow ends on the right side.
Weir Sta US	219	Upstream station for weir flow starts.
Weir Submerg	100	The ratio of the downstream depth above the weir to the upstream depth above the weir.
Wr Top Wdth	102	Top width of water over the weir.
WS Air Entr.	181	Water surface elevation accounting for air entrainment.
WS Inlet	245	WS at the inlet of a pump station.
WS Outlet	246	WS at the outlet of a pump station.
WSPRO EG	112	Energy grade elevation upstream of bridge for the WSPRO method.
WSPRO WS	105	Water surface elevation upstream of bridge for the WSPRO method.
XS Delta EG	163	Change in energy gradeline between current section and next one downstream.
XS Delta WS	162	Change in water surface between current section and next one downstream.

| Yarnell EG | 111 | Energy grade elevation upstream of bridge for Yarnell method. |
| Yarnell WS | 104 | Water surface elevation upstream of bridge for Yarnell method. |

Made in the USA
Lexington, KY
26 January 2016